MEDICAL MUSIC THERAPY:

A Meta-Analysis
&
Agenda for
Future Research

Cheryl Dileo & Joke Bradt

Jeffrey Books

MEDICAL MUSIC THERAPY:
A Meta-Analysis
&
Agenda for
Future Research

ISBN   0-9770278-3-X

Distributed throughout the world by:
Jeffrey Books
538 Covered Bridge Rd.
Cherry Hill, NJ, USA 08034
Fax: 856-354-8706

Cover design by Felice Macera © 2005

Table of Contents

Dedication

This book is dedicated to:

Charles Braswell,
my teacher, mentor, role model and friend,
with love and deepest gratitude
...for inspiring me to be a music therapist,
...for wisdom, guidance and support throughout the years,
...and for instilling in me a love of research.
Your influence on my life has been profound.
cd

and to

Felice Macera,
my loving husband,
for your patience, understanding and inspiration.
jb

Acknowledgements

The following present and former PhD students in Music Therapy at Temple University contributed immeasurably to the present volume through literature searches, article retrieval, data coding and suggestions for future research: *Elaine Abbott, Yadira Albornoz, Joy Allen, Kat Avins, Nadine Cadesky, John Carpente, Michelle Cooper, Bridget Doak, Lillian Eyre, James Hiller, Nancy Jackson, Roberta Kagin, Dr. Douglas Keith, John Mahoney, Bryan Muller, Kathleen Murphy, Carol Shultis, Victoria Vega, and Michael Zanders.* I am deeply appreciative not only for your keen insights, research skills and dedication to music therapy, but also for the privilege of calling you "my students."

I am grateful to Felice Macera for the beautiful cover design, for the photographs and for his generous and abundant help.

Without the support of the people who have shared my life, this book would not have been possible. Thank you Mom and Dad, Jeff, Linda, Dawn, Natxo, Lucanne, Julia and Janice. A special thanks to my son, Jeff, for his love, humor, patience, sensitivity and medical knowledge. No mother could be more proud than I.

My clinical work in medical music therapy is always the source of my motivation to conduct research and to find new and better ways to work. Each patient I have had the honor to meet in music has influenced my research and has touched my heart.

My co-author, colleague and friend, Joke Bradt, has been the "statistical genius" behind this book. Her work ethic and dedication to this project have been more than I could have ever hoped for. And even more importantly, her warmth and caring have made every minute of working together a true joy.

And lastly and above all, I thank my Creator for His many blessings.

cd
October, 2005

* * * * * * * * * *

I would like to express my appreciation to Mary Delacy Kidwell. Your continued patience and calm during the endless hours of inputting the research data were remarkable - thank you.

Dr. Bruce Rind, your advice and guidance with effect size computation issues was invaluable. Thank you also for lending us your meta-analysis software program for the pilot study.

A special thanks goes to Drs. Mark W. Lipsey and David B. Wilson for creating and giving free access to their SPSS Macros for meta-analysis. But more importantly, thank you for your willingness to readily offer advice and solutions for our meta-analytic questions. Your help was essential for the completion of this project.

My deepest thanks are expressed to Felice Macera, my wonderful husband, for all of your technical support during the pilot stage of this research and for your creativity in designing the book cover. Thank you also, for your tolerance and patience during all the hours I spent on this seemingly endless project. You instilled in me perseverance and indomitable spirit – without it, I could have not completed this research.

Gabriella and Elisa, my two beautiful daughters: your joy, excitement, and carefree minds provide me with energy and help me put things into perspective.

And finally, Cheryl Dileo, my mentor, colleague, friend and co-author: you have inspired me from the first day I entered this country because of your passion for music therapy, your dedication to your students, your scholarship and your incredible work ethic. I am deeply grateful for your support of my growth as a clinician and a scholar. It was an honor to work so intensely with you on this project. Your friendship and continuous encouragements throughout were invaluable.

jb
October, 2005

About the Authors

Cheryl Dileo, PhD, MT-BC, is Professor of Music Therapy, Coordinator of the Master's Program in Music Therapy, and Director of the new, interdisciplinary Arts and Quality of Life Research Center at Temple University in Philadelphia. She is a former McAndless Distinguished Professor and Chair in the Humanities of Eastern Michigan University and has taught at Loyola University of the South and the University of Evansville, where she founded the music therapy program. She developed and directs the Music Therapy Programs at Temple University Hospital and is a music therapist at Compassionate Care Hospice. She has served as President of the World Federation of Music Therapy and the National Association for Music Therapy and has held numerous positions within these organizations. Currently, she is the Business Manager of the World Federation of Music Therapy and Co-Chair of the Ethics Board of the American Music Therapy Association. She received her Bachelor's and Master's degrees in music therapy from Loyola University of the South, and her PhD from Louisiana State University. She is a grant reviewer for the National Institutes of Health, the National Center for Complementary and Alternative Medicine and the National Cancer Institute. She is the Principal Investigator of a large grant from the State of PA to support research concerning the effects of music therapy on multicultural inpatients with cancer or heart disease. She is the author/editor of 12 books and over 90 journal articles and book chapters. She has lectured extensively in the US and around the world. Her research topics include: medical music therapy (oncology and cardiology), music therapy in palliative care, music therapy in pain and stress management, multicultural music therapy, international music therapy practice, education and training in music therapy and professional ethics.

Joke Bradt, PhD, MT-BC, is Assistant Professor and Coordinator of Music Therapy at Montclair State University, New Jersey. She has taught at a variety of music therapy programs in Europe and has presented more than 50 lectures and workshops at regional, national as well as international music therapy conferences. She has given multiple presentations at past World Congresses of Music Therapy (Washington, 1999; Oxford, 2002) and was the keynote speaker and presenter at the Fifth Italian Congress of Music Therapy (Rimini, 2003). After earning her Master of Music Pedagogy degree from the prestigious Lemmensinstituut in Belgium, she was twice awarded a Fulbright Scholarship to study music therapy at Temple University, where she earned her Master of Music Therapy degree. Upon completion of her graduate studies, she returned to Belgium where she developed and implemented two clinical music therapy programs. She later came back to Temple University to further develop her research skills and obtain her PhD. Since 1997, she has been focusing her work on medical music therapy and research. She has authored and co-authored several book chapters, including "Entrainment, Resonance, and Pain-Related Suffering" (in C. Dileo (1999), *Music Therapy & Medicine*), "Meta-Analysis" (in B. Wheeler (2005), *Music Therapy Research, 2nd ed.)*, "Music Therapy: Applications to Stress Management" (in P. Lehrer & Woolfolk (in press), *Principles and Practice of Stress Management, 3rd ed*) and "The Voice of Women Suffering from Chronic Pain" (in S. Hadley (in press), *Music Therapy: Feminist Perspectives and Critiques*). She is an Executive Board Member of the Mid-Atlantic Regional Chapter of the American Music Therapy Association and is the Mid-Atlantic Region Student Affairs Advisor. In addition, she has served on the self-assessment examination committee of the Certification Board for Music Therapists as well as on the NJ Taskforce for Occupational Regulation for Music Therapy. As a clinician, she currently works with children with communication difficulties and women with chronic pain.

INTRODUCTION

Why Meta-Analysis?

Research concerning the effects of music and music therapy for medical patients has burgeoned during the past 20 years. Several thousand clinical and research articles have been published during this time in a wide range of medical specialty areas. The clinical literature is extremely diverse in terms of: music or music therapy intervention used, theoretical orientation underlying practice, medical population, subjects' ages, clinical condition, and intended outcomes. There is a similar diversity in the experimental research literature. Within a multitude of research designs, subjects of varying ages with a wide range of medical conditions have received an array of music or music therapy interventions intended to ameliorate physiological, psychological, social, cognitive and/or spiritual issues. Music therapists are challenged in summarizing music or music therapy's effects in these domains across populations, age ranges and medical conditions, as research results vary accordingly.

Whereas traditional literature reviews are useful in providing an overview of the research that has been conducted, they are ineffective in helping researchers draw valid conclusions concerning music or music therapy's effects. Meta-analysis, a scientifically rigorous type of literature review aimed at synthesizing findings across a number of studies, provides one way of answering the basic question: "Is music therapy effective?"

In addition, because music therapy research is typically characterized by the use of small samples, statistically significant results may not be achieved. Even if the intervention is effective and the study is well designed, a non-significant p-value may result, leading to the erroneous conclusion that music therapy is not an effective treatment intervention (Gold, 2004).

Meta-analysis provides a means of quantifying and translating the results of separate research studies into a standard measure of effect (Durlak, Meerson & Foster, 2003). Thus, meta-analysis allows for "combining the numerical results of studies with disparate, even conflicting, research methods and findings; it enables researchers to discover the consistencies in a set of seemingly inconsistent findings and to arrive at conclusions more accurate and credible than those presented in any one of the primary studies" (Hunt, 1997, p. 1). Meta-analysis procedures also allow researchers to identify the variables (called moderator variables) that influence the potential inconsistency of results across studies.

A key concept in meta-analysis procedures is that of a standard effect size (ES). "The prime advantage of an ES is its ability to translate the magnitude of effect into a standardized common metric across studies" (Durlak, et al., 2003, p. 245). Thus, these procedures permit a "common language among tongues" (Dileo & Bradt, 2005, p. 282).

There are both advantages and limitations to using meta-analysis as a means of research synthesis. Its advantages include: 1) the rigor of the method, 2) its sensitivity to effects from individual studies, 3) its ability to "weight" findings according to sample size, 4) its statistical power (greater than in individual studies), and 5) its utility in identifying foci for future research (Dileo & Bradt, 2005). Its disadvantages include: 1) its need for extensive time and labor commitments, 2) its potential bias towards published vs. unpublished studies or studies in one language only, 3) its potential to combine studies that are extremely disparate and consequently meaningless, 4) its potential inclusion of studies with limited internal validity (Dileo & Bradt, 2005). However, researchers may directly minimize these limitations by carefully delineating inclusion and exclusion criteria for potential studies.

Steps in the Meta-Analysis Process

There are five major steps in conducting a scientifically rigorous meta-analysis:

1. Identify a clear research question(s).
2. Conduct a thorough literature review (published, gray and unpublished literature) implementing detailed inclusion/exclusion criteria.
3. Extract pre-identified information from each study in an accurate and reliable manner.
4. Apply statistical procedures for determining the effect size, homogeneity and data comparisons.
5. Evaluate the results, formulate conclusions and make recommendations for further research (Dileo & Bradt, 2005; Durlak, et al., 2003).

Meta-Analysis in Music Therapy

A number of researchers have utilized meta-analysis procedures to examine the effects of music therapy on various clinical conditions. A summary of these studies is presented in Table 1.

Based on the information in Table 1, it is not unreasonable to state that meta-analytic reviews are becoming more commonplace in music therapy, and it is expected that these reviews will be published with greater frequency in the music therapy literature in years to come. Moreover, as the emphasis on evidence-based practice grows, music therapists will be called upon more often to document the effectiveness of music therapy to current and potential employers, third-party payers, regulatory bodies as well as clients and their families.

Table 1

A Summary of Meta-Analytic Research in Music Therapy

Author(s)	Year(s)	Topic
Standley	1986, 1992, 1996, 2000	Medical/dental treatment
Standley	2002	Neonatal intensive care
Koger, Chapin & Brotons	1999	Dementia
Silverman	2003	Psychosis
Pelletier	2004	Stress Reduction
Whipple	2004	Autism
Gold, Voracek & Wigram	2004	Children/Adolescents with Psychopathology
Gold & Wigram	2005	Autism Spectrum Disorder
Maratos & Gold	2005	Depression
Gold, Heldal, Dahle & Wigram	In progress	Schizophrenia

METHOD

Background

During the past 15 years, the first author has been compiling literature on medical music therapy through annual literature searches. Several thousand articles have been accumulated, and these are used routinely for teaching purposes in medical music therapy courses at Temple University. This literature was overwhelming to say the least, and the first author felt challenged in finding ways to organize and synthesize its information. Of interest was the identification of physiological, psychological, cognitive, social and spiritual variables most readily (and least readily) influenced by music therapy or music medicine interventions (those involving pre-recorded music listening experiences administered by medical personnel). In addition, she was very interested in categorizing and analyzing the research according to the type of intervention used: music medicine vs. music therapy. More specifically, she wanted to examine whether music therapy interventions were as effective, more effective or less effective than music medicine interventions. It was felt that this information was extremely important both for the medical establishment and for the music therapy profession. A parallel goal was to more clearly define the parameters and methods of medical music therapy and music medicine for students, clinicians, and employers with the ultimate intent of establishing levels of practice and corresponding needs for advanced training. Also, as the literature on music medicine was much larger than the medical music therapy literature, it appeared significant to develop a research agenda for future medical music therapy research.

The impetus for the current study, which first began in 2001, was this author's teaching of the doctoral course, "Research in Music and Medicine." She thought that conducting a meta-analysis as a class project would provide a worthwhile learning endeavor for the students involved (much to their dismay). Besides instructing students in meta-analysis procedures, it was felt that the process of searching the literature, analyzing and extracting information from each article and making recommendations for future research would provide an excellent learning tool. The second author served as a teaching assistant for this class and instructed students in procedures for collecting statistical data from the studies. Students posted information from each article on the "Blackboard" website, and engaged in stimulating discussions about the state of the research. The meta-analysis was not completed at that time, and two subsequent doctoral-level "Research in Music and Medicine" classes participated in bringing this project to fruition. Several versions of the meta-analysis were prepared, presented at conferences, and updated.

One reality of doing this type of research is the fact that it never ends! There are always more studies to add as they are published, and additional analyses on the data to be conducted. In 2004, the authors decided to discontinue updating the literature and to begin writing a final version of their research, and it is this version that comprises the current text.

METHOD

Research Questions

Several research questions were investigated in this study:

1. How effective are music medicine or music therapy interventions in the treatment of patients (according to 11 medical specializations), regardless of the types of outcome measures employed?
> Is there a difference in the effects of music medicine vs. music therapy?

2. How effective are music medicine or music therapy interventions in influencing specific outcome measures in these medical populations?
> Is there a difference in the effects of music medicine vs. music therapy?

3. Do any of the following factors influence the results of treatment?
> a. Type of music intervention (listening, music & relaxation, music & imagery, active music-making, or combinations thereof)
> b. Category of intervention (music medicine vs. music therapy)
> c. Musical preference (patient preferred or non-preferred)
> d. Medical population (11 medical specialties)
> e. Level of randomization (randomized, non-randomized, within-subjects or randomization unknown)

Literature Search

Utilizing the first author's extensive bibliography on the topic as a starting point, extensive searches were conducted by the authors and Ph.D. students at Temple University. All of the relevant standard databases were searched (e.g., Medline, PsycInfo, Ovid, CINAHL, etc.) using only the keyword, "music" in addition to a variety of other combinations of keywords involving music (e.g., music and anxiety; music and pain). In this way, the largest number of articles could be retrieved. In addition, the non-indexed music therapy and music therapy-related journals were hand-searched for studies, along with music therapy books. Finally, a search was conducted for master's theses and dissertations using standard databases and music therapy databases at Temple University. Once these large lists of articles were identified, the first author reviewed them to determine which articles were relevant to the analysis. (It is noted that a search using "music" only as a keyword yields many types of studies, including: those relevant to the medical problems of musicians, historical articles on the medical problems of famous composers, and a host of studies on music perception and cognition to name a few categories). These references were then inputted into the master bibliography (which had been organized according to 11 medical specialty areas: see Table 2 below). Articles that were found to be relevant were retrieved in hard copy (with the exception of theses and dissertations).

Table 2
Description of Medical Specialty Areas

Specialization	Description
Surgery	Includes: pre-, peri- or post-surgical interventions with all age groups; various types of anesthesia (e.g., regional, general); and surgical procedures involving many specialty areas (e.g., gynecology, cardiology)
Cardiology/ICU	Includes: treatment for cardiac illness and cardiac rehabilitation, and acute treatment in intensive care units (cardiac, mechanical ventilation); adults only
Cancer/Terminal Illness/HIV	Includes: all age groups with cancer, HIV or terminal condition; active treatment procedures or palliative care
Fetal	Includes prenatal infant and maternal responses
Neonatology	Includes premature infants and full-term neonates
OB/GYN	Includes: labor and delivery, gynecological procedures and c-section
Pediatrics	Includes: various procedures and medical conditions in children
Rehabilitation	Includes: physical, speech and neurological rehabilitation and acute and chronic pain conditions
Alzheimer's	Includes: patients with Alzheimer's disease and other forms of dementia
Dental	Includes: dental procedures for all age groups
General Hospital	Includes adults undergoing various medical procedures (not included in other categories)

The medical specialization categories established were by no means mutually exclusive. The content of many studies overlapped into two or three categories. For example, a study dealing with cardiac surgery in children could have been placed in the "Surgery" category, the "Pediatrics" category or the "Cardiology/ICU" category. An attempt was made to place most of the surgery articles into the "Surgery" category, and most of the articles dealing with children (with the exception of newborns) into the "Pediatrics" category. The "General Hospital" category was created to include medical specializations (i.e., medical procedures) represented by only one or two studies, and therefore may be considered a "Miscellaneous" category. An attempt was made to limit the overall number of categories so that each would contain a sufficient number of studies to allow statistical comparisons among them.

Inclusion/Exclusion Criteria

After hard copies of articles were retrieved, each was reviewed to determine if it met the predetermined criteria for inclusion in the meta-analysis. Specifically, to be included, each study must have been designed to test the following:

1) A music medicine or music therapy treatment condition or group vs. a no-treatment control condition or group.
2) A music medicine or music therapy treatment compared to other types of treatments (e.g., massage, multi-sensory stimulation) if a no-treatment control group was used and statistical data comparing the music medicine or music therapy treatment group with the no-treatment control group were provided (in these cases only data for the music medicine or music therapy treatment vs. the control treatment were used, and the sample size was adjusted accordingly).

Thus, eligible designs included pretest-posttest control group designs and within-subjects designs if a no-treatment control condition was used.

Study designs that did not contain the aforementioned criteria were excluded. In addition, studies were excluded for the following reasons:

1) Lack of sufficient statistical information (i.e., sample sizes, standard deviations) in published studies and in dissertation abstracts.
2) Use of a music or music therapy treatment combined with another intervention (e.g., music and suggestion).
3) Use of laboratory conditions (e.g., simulated pain) or non-medical subjects.
4) Use of applied behavioral analysis designs.
5) Publication in a foreign language with no English abstract.

Applying these criteria resulted in 183 studies that were eligible for inclusion in the current meta-analytic review.

Coding of Studies

For each study, the following information was extracted and coded (Table 3).

Table 3
Information Coded

Author, Year, Source and Reference	Type of Medical Patient (medical specialty)
Ages of Subjects	Type/Description of Experimental Design
Number of Experimental Groups	Independent Variables (Music Treatment)
Type of Music Intervention (Listening, etc.)	Category of Intervention (Music Medicine vs. Music Therapy)
Dependent Variable(s)	Musical Preference (Patient-Preferred vs. Non-Preferred Music Used)
Use/Type of Randomization	All statistics (i.e., Means, SDs, t tests, F ratios, correlations, chi-squares, df, statistical significance and sample sizes)

Studies were categorized as "music medicine" according to the following criteria: 1) use of passive listening music interventions of pre-recorded music and 2) music intervention implemented by medical personnel (non-music therapists). In contrast, studies were categorized as "music therapy" if: 1) a music therapist implemented an "in-person" treatment intervention and 2) music therapy methods were used. In some studies, music therapists provided a pre-recorded music listening experience as the intervention, and these studies were classified as music medicine. The latter categorization was made in an attempt to make a distinction between the therapeutic effects of music itself as an intervention, and the effects of music therapy (involving a relationship between client and therapist, a therapeutic process and a "live" music experience). The distinction between music therapy and music medicine can often become quite blurred. These categories were defined as such for purposes of this study only, and discussion of further distinctions, levels of practice and requirements for advanced training will be the topics of future publications.

It is noted that the amount of information provided concerning the music medicine or music therapy treatment varied widely among the studies used, therefore simple and straightforward criteria for categorizing these types of interventions were adopted. Also, not all studies included specific details concerning how the music was selected. In some cases, a variety of music selections were offered to the patient, and the patient chose music according to his or her preference (these were coded as patient-preferred music studies). In other cases, the musical preference of the patient was not a consideration, and all subjects were offered the same music (these were coded as patient non-preferred music studies). Moreover, some studies provided no information at all concerning the music intervention (these were coded as "no information available" studies).

Studies Used

As mentioned previously, 183 usable studies were identified for inclusion in the current meta-analysis. These appeared between 1963 and 2003, and comprised: 167 published studies, 10 unpublished dissertations, 5 unpublished master's theses and 1 unpublished paper. Some published articles reported data for more than one study with different numbers of subjects in each and separate statistical analyses for the data. Thus, these studies were treated as separate and distinct in calculating the total number of studies.

The number of studies included in each medical specialty area is listed in Table 4. Sample sizes of studies ranged from 5 to 500 subjects (Table 5) and totaled 7894 subjects for this meta-analytic review.

Table 4
Number of Studies Included for Each Medical Specialty Area

Medical Specialization	Number of Studies Included
Surgery	51
Cardiology/ICU	14
Cancer/Terminal Ill./HIV	18
Fetal	4
Neonatology	17
OB/GYN	7
Pediatrics	11
Rehabilitation	18
Alzheimer's	26
Dental	6
General Hospital	11

Table 5
Sample Sizes for Studies in Each Medical Specialty Area

Population	Range	Mean	S.D
Surgery	9-180	54.49	35.08
Cardiology/ICU	20-140	47.57	35.52
Cancer/Term.Ill./HIV	6-97	34.26	25.57
Fetal	11-34	20.25	9.87
General Hospital	30-193	63.91	46.41
Neonatology	12-153	52.65	47.53
OB/GYN	7-500	91.14	180.56
Pediatrics	10-40	26.45	10.71
Dentistry	24-80	51.83	23.21
Alzheimer's	5-43	21.04	10.41
Rehabilitation	5-42	20.67	9.37

Because of the breadth of medical issues addressed across the 11 medical specialty areas, it was not surprising when coding procedures yielded approximately 180 different dependent variables for this meta-analysis, with most studies examining effects of treatment on multiple variables. In addition, the terminology used for dependent variables differed across the studies (e.g., "mood" and "affect") and was at times very general, although the research outcome was similar in purpose. To better manage these data in the statistical process, similar variables were grouped together into categories (Table 6). In addition, a number of dependent variables were excluded from the analysis if they were measured in only one study (e.g., vascular flow, cerebral perfusion pressure, helplessness, etc.), because single-study variables are precluded in meta-analysis procedures. Needless to say, there is an inherent risk in categorizing similar variables, i.e., in mixing "apples and oranges." Thus, the reader is cautioned in advance to this potential problem. The final list of the 40 dependent variables used in the current study is presented in Table 7. The diversity of these variables is noteworthy, as they comprise physiological, psychological, cognitive, behavioral and social domains, as well as drug intake and cost-effectiveness data.

Statistical Analysis

Computation of Effect Sizes

The statistic used for the calculation of effect size in this review was r, the Pearson correlation coefficient. Preference was given to r over d because of the inability to compute d accurately when authors fail to report the sample sizes of the experimental and/or control group; unfortunately, this omission is not uncommon in the literature. For discussion on additional reasons for preferring r over d, the reader is referred to Rosenthal (1991).

Formulas for calculating r were taken from Rosenthal (1984, 1991) to obtain an effect size r for each dependent variable included in each study. The r

value ranges from –1.00 to +1.00. A positive value indicates that the effect is in the predicted direction (as set forth by the hypothesis); a negative sign reflects an effect in the direction that was not predicted. In most cases, a positive number indicates that the experimental or treatment group performed better than the control group on the dependent variable, whereas a negative number reflects that the control group showed greater improvement on the outcome measure (Dileo & Bradt, 2005). An interpretation of effect size has been proposed by Cohen (1977) and is widely accepted (Table 8).

Table 6
Categories of Dependent Variables

Dependent Variable	Includes:
Heart Rate	Heart rate, pulse rate
Skin temperature	Skin temperature, finger temperature
Mean Arterial Pressure	Mean Arterial Pressure, Arterial Pressure
Analgesics	Including Morphine, Alfentanil, Ketobemidone, 'opioid use'
Sedatives	Including Fentanyl, Midazolam, 'sedatives'
Anesthetic Drugs	Including Isoflurane
Anxiety	Anxiety, stress
Hospital stay	Hospital stay, duration of PACU stay, length of stay
Sleep	Duration of sleep, quality of sleep, sleepfulness
Galvanic Skin Resistance	Galvanic skin resistance, electrodermal activity
Cortisol	Cortisol, plasma cortisol
Aggression	Aggression, aggressive behaviors, hostility
Cognitive functioning	Cognitive functioning, recall, test scores, cognitive testing scores
Mood	Mood, positive affect, negative affect, affect, Profile of Mood State scores
Social behaviors	Social behaviors, socialization, social interaction, participation
Speech	Speech rate, speech content, verbal intelligibility, verbal responses
Gait	Velocity, cadence, stride length, symmetry
Distress	Distress, crying
Weight	Weight, weight loss, weight gain
Motor Activity	Motor Activity, gross motor limb activity, movement, gross motor activity

Table 7
List of 40 Dependent Variables Included in Current Study

Heart Rate	Weight Gain
Respiration Rate	Sleep
Diastolic Blood Pressure	Fatigue
Systolic Blood Pressure	Motor Activity
Blood Pressure (non-specific)	In-Seat Behavior
Mean Arterial Pressure	Gait
Skin Temperature	Length of Hospital Stay
Galvanic Skin Resistance	Anxiety (STAI)
Oxygen Saturation Level	Anxiety (Non-STAI)
Secretory IgA	Distress
Cortisol Level	Agitation
Epinephrine Level	Aggression
Norepinephrine Level	Depression
Analgesic Drug Intake	Mood
Sedative Drug Intake	Feelings of Control
Anesthetic Drug Intake	Well-Being/Life Satisfaction
Pain	Social Interaction
Comfort Level	Speech/Verbalization
Nausea/Vomiting	Attention
Food Intake	Cognitive Functioning

Table 8
Interpretation of Effect Size

Small	Moderate	Large
$r = .10$	$r = .25$	$r = .40$
$d = .20$	$d = .50$	$d = .80$

A "symptom-level" effect size was computed for each dependent variable included in each study. When a study included multiple outcome measures for the same dependent variable (e.g., different scales to measure pain), an effect size was calculated for each outcome measure, and a mean effect size was then computed. This calculation was needed to assure that each study contributed the same number of data points, (a phenomenon critical to establishing accuracy of the meta-analytic procedures) for a specific dependent variable (Durlak, et al., 2003). Including multiple data points from one study to a meta-analytic procedure would result in an inflated sample size and an overrepresentation of those studies that contribute additional effect sizes. Finally, a sample-level effect size (averaging all the effect sizes within each study) was calculated for each of the 183 studies.

It is important to point out that for many studies, the effect size computation may have underestimated the true effect size(s). Unfortunately, in many music medicine and music therapy studies, statistical reporting was often limited to statements such as "no significant difference was found." When this occurred, a $Z = 0$ was assigned to the outcome measure in question, resulting in $r = .00$. For most of these studies, however, an effect size larger than zero would have been calculated if more detailed statistics had been provided. In other instances, the only statistical information provided was $p < .05$. In these cases, the most conservative p value, ($p = .05$), was employed in the computation of the effect size. This scenario is also unfortunate as it often results in an underestimation of the true effect size. However, such a conservative approach is necessary in cases of poor statistical reporting (Rosenthal, 1991).

Meta-Analytic Procedures

Prior to statistical analyses, Fisher's Z_r-transformations were applied to the correlation coefficient r. After these analyses, the Z_r-transformations were converted back into their original metrics, r, to present the results. This conversion is necessary to deal with the problematic standard error formulation that would result from using the correlational coefficient in its standard form (Lipsey & Wilson, 2001).

The following meta-analytic procedures were then conducted to address the research questions:

1. Computation of a weighted mean sample-level effect size across medical specialties (each of the 183 studies contributed one sample-level effect size);
2. Computation of a weighted mean sample-level effect size per each medical specialty;
3. Computation of weighted mean symptom-level effect sizes across medical specialties;
4. Computation of weighted mean symptom-level effect size per medical specialty.

The *SPSS Macros for Meta-Analysis,* developed by Lipsey and Wilson (2001), were used for these computations. In calculating the mean effect size, each contributing effect size was weighted by its inverse variance. This procedure gives greater weight to effect sizes based on larger samples as opposed to smaller samples, making the contribution of an effect size to a statistical analysis proportional to its reliability (Lipsey & Wilson, 2001). Subsequently, a confidence interval (*c.i.*) was determined for each mean effect size. This confidence interval portrays the range of effects one might expect at a p level of .05. If the resulting *c.i.* did not include zero, the mean effect size was statistically significant, meaning that the treatment and the control group differed significantly from each other. Finally, a test for homogeneity for the distribution of effect sizes was conducted.

For each of the analyses, the following statistics were reported (Table 9):

Table 9
Statistics Reported for Each Analysis

k reflects the number of studies included in the analysis.

N reflects the total sample size of the analysis.

r_u is the unbiased or weighted effect size.

95% c.i.. The confidence interval at the $p = .05$ level

p indicates the level of significance

Q is the homogeneity statistic.
(An asterisk following the Q-value indicates that homogeneity was rejected or that the studies are heterogeneous).

Homogeneity

Homogeneity was challenged in many of the sub-analyses conducted in this study, i.e., the effect sizes for specific dependent measures were inconsistent across studies. This was anticipated, as the studies varied greatly in terms of study characteristics. Even though the analyses were grouped according to medical specialty, many other factors were expected to contribute to between-study variability. These factors included: a) type of treatment intervention, b) category of intervention (music medicine or music therapy), d) use of preferred vs. non-preferred music, e) subject age and diagnosis, (f) stage and severity of illness, g) study design, h) level of randomization, i) subjects' musical backgrounds, etc. Few studies included information on all of these factors. In addition, other important information concerning study characteristics was often missing. Because of this problem, homogeneity of sub-group data is not often achieved in meta-analytic studies, and frequently, researchers must interpret results from a group of heterogeneous studies (Durlak, et al., 2003).

In meta-analytic procedures, it is also necessary to examine the distribution of effect sizes to determine if outliers are present. In the current study, when outliers were identified, they were removed from the analyses. This often resulted in homogeneity. At times, however, heterogeneity remained even after exclusion of the outlier(s). In other cases, no clear outliers could be identified because of a wide variability of effect sizes. In these instances, analyses were performed to identify possible moderator variables or variables that could account for the excess variability.

Moderator Variables

It is important for researchers and clinicians to understand the factors that contribute to or diminish the effectiveness of an intervention. Moderator analyses thus may permit a better understanding of the true effects of music therapy or music medicine interventions in medical settings. In the current analysis, when a significant Q-value remained associated with a mean effect size after exclusion of extreme values (indicating heterogeneity), a mixed-effects model was applied to the data. A mixed-effects model operates on the premise that the variance beyond subject-level sampling error is derived: 1) in part from systematic factors that can be identified and 2) in part from random factors. Thus, there is the assumption that certain identifiable study characteristics act as moderator variables and are associated with systematic differences between and among the effect sizes. To accomplish this analysis, Wilson and Lipsey's (2001) "SPSS Macro for Analog to the Analysis of Variance (mixed effects)" was used. This macro is based on the meta-analysis technique developed by Hodges (1982) which groups the effect sizes in mutually exclusive categories on the basis of an independent or categorical variable, and tests both the homogeneity among the effect sizes within the categories as well as the differences between the categories. If the between-category variance (Q_b) is statistically significant, the mean effect sizes across groups differ by more than sampling error. This means that the categorical variable partly explains the excess variability in the observed effect sizes (Lipsey & Wilson, 2001).

It is important to point out that the Q-test has low statistical power for rejecting homogeneity when only a small number of effect sizes are calculated, and especially when these are based on small samples. To be conservative, a mixed effects model was applied to the data based on few effect sizes and small samples. At times, moderator variables were identified, even if homogeneity had not been rejected by the Q-test.

3

META-ANALYSIS RESULTS

Sample-Level Results

Sample-Level Effect Sizes

Table 10 lists all studies with their sample-level effect size in descending order according to effect size magnitude. The effect sizes ranged from $r = .97$ to $r = -.20$. For 143 studies, a positive sample-level effect size was found. For 36 studies, a sample-level effect size of $r = .00$ was found. However, for many of these studies, the conservative $Z = 0$ was assigned to the data because of the lack of statistical information, resulting in an $r = .00$. If more detailed statistics had been available, fewer studies would have contained the sample-level effect size of zero. Only 3 studies reported a negative sample-level effect size.

A variety of music interventions were used in these studies: music listening ($k = 140$), music and imagery ($k = 5$), active music making ($k = 16$), music therapy sessions, including a variety of interventions ($k = 20$), and music and relaxation ($k = 2$). Seventy-six studies implemented patient-preferred music, and 75 studies did not take patients' preferences into account. For 32 studies, this information was unknown or irrelevant. Studies were coded as either music medicine ($k = 129$) or music therapy ($k = 54$). Ninety-two studies utilized random sampling procedures, 24 studies used non-random sampling, and 53 studies used a within-subjects design. For 13 studies, the level of randomization was not specified.

A total of 98 population-specific analyses (medical specialties) and 33 across-population (dependent variables) analyses were conducted.

Table 10
Sample-Level Effect Sizes in Descending Order of Magnitude

Author	Year	Medical Specialty	Source	N	Study Design	Music[1] Experience	r
Allen, et al.	2001	Surgery	Journal	40	Exp-contr	M.L.	0.97
Brotons & Pickett-Cooper	1996	Alzheimer's	Journal	20	Within Ss	Music Tx	0.93
Updike & Charles	1987	Surgery	Journal	10	Exp-contr	M.L.	0.90
Lord & Garner	1993	Alzheimer's	Journal	40	Exp-contr	Active music	0.86
Thomas, et al.	1997	Alzheimer's	Journal	14	Within Ss	M.L.	0.84
Snyder & Olsen	1996	Alzheimer's	Journal	5	Within Ss	M.L.	0.81
Sontag, et al.	1969	Fetal	Journal	11	Within Ss	M.L.	0.79

Ammon	1968	Pediatrics	Journal	20	Exp-contr	M.L.	0.78
Thaut, et al.	1993	Rehabilitation	Journal	10	Within Ss	M.L.	0.77
Olderog-Millard & Smith	1989	Alzheimer's	Journal	10	Within Ss	Active music	0.76
Gerdner	2000	Alzheimer's	Journal	39	Within Ss	M.L.	0.76
Clair	1996	Alzheimer's	Journal	26	Within Ss	Active music	0.76
Hanser, et al.	1983	OB/GYN	Journal	7	Within Ss	Music Tx	0.74
Schorr	1993	Rehabilitation	Journal	30	Within Ss	M.L.	0.73
Chlan	1998	Cardiology/ ICU	Journal	35	Exp-contr	M.L.	0.72
Goddaer & Abraham	1994	Alzheimer's	Journal	29	Within Ss	M.L.	0.72
Szeto & Yung	1999	Surgery	Journal	9	Exp-contr	M.L.	0.68
Wolfe	1983	Alzheimer's	Journal	22	Exp-contr	Music Tx	0.67
Magee & Davidson	2002	Rehabilitation	Journal	14	Within Ss	Music Tx	0.66
Froehlich	1984	Pediatrics	Journal	40	Exp-contr	Music Tx	0.65
Butt & Kisilevsky	2000	Neonatology	Journal	14	Within Ss	M.L.	0.65
Bradt	2001	Pediatrics	Dissert.	32	Exp-contr	Music Tx	0.64
Standley & Moore	1995	Neonatology	Journal	20	Within Ss	M.L.	0.64
Satt	1984	Fetal	Dissert.	16	Exp-contr	M.L.	0.64
Zimmer, et al.	1982	Fetal	Journal	20	Within Ss	M.L.	0.63
Clair	1997	Alzheimer's	Journal	12	Within Ss	Active music	0.61
Stanley & Ramsey	1998	Rehabilitation	Journal	20	Exp-contr	Active music	0.59
Miluk-Kolasa, et al.	2002	Surgery	Journal	89	Exp-contr	M.L.	0.58
Wong, et al.	2001	Cardiology/ ICU	Journal	20	Within Ss	M.L.	0.58
Mullooly, et al.	1988	Surgery	Journal	28	Exp-contr	M.L.	0.58
Korb	1997	Alzheimer's	Journal	9	Within Ss	Active music	0.58
Standley	2000	Neonatology	Chapter	12	Within Ss	M.L.	0.57
Robb	2000	Pediatrics	Journal	10	Within Ss	Music Tx	0.57
Locsin	1981	Surgery	Journal	24	Exp-contr	M.L.	0.55
Miluk-Kolosa, et al.	1996	Surgery	Journal	100	Exp-contr	M.L.	0.55
Foster & Valentine	2001	Alzheimer's	Journal	23	Exp-contr	M.L.	0.54
Updike	1990	Cardiology/ ICU	Journal	20	Exp-contr	M.L.	0.53
Brackbill, et al.	1966	Neonatology	Journal	24	Within Ss	M.L.	0.53
Brotons & Koger	2000	Alzheimer's	Journal	20	Within Ss	Active music	0.52
Angus & Faux	1989	Surgery	Chapter	26	Within-Ss	M.L.	0.52
Kaminski & Hall	1996	Neonatology	Journal	20	Within Ss	M.L.	0.52

Bonny	1983	Cardiology/ICU	Journal	20	Within Ss	M.L.	0.52
Frank	1985	Cancer/Term. Ill/HIV	Journal	15	Within Ss	Music Imag.	0.52
Walther-Larsen, et al.	1988	Surgery	Journal	64	Exp-contr	M.L.	0.52
Zimmerman, et al.	1989	Cancer/Term. Ill/HIV	Journal	40	Exp-contr	M.L.	0.50
Suzuki	1998	Alzheimer's	Journal	8	Within Ss	Active music	0.50
Pfaff, et al.	1989	Cancer/Term. Ill/HIV	Journal	6	Within Ss	M.L.	0.49
Anderson & Baron	1991	Dentistry	Journal	36	Exp-contr	M.L.	0.48
Ragneskog, et al.	1996	Alzheimer's	Journal	20	Within Ss	M.L.	0.47
Nayak, et al.	2000	Rehabilitation	Journal	18	Exp-contr	Active music	0.47
Grasso, et al.	2000	Pediatrics	Journal	20	Exp-contr	M.L.	0.46
Clark, et al.	1998	Alzheimer's	Journal	18	Within Ss	M.L.	0.46
Joyce, et al.	2001	Neonatology	Journal	23	Exp-contr	M.L.	0.46
Malone	1996	Pediatrics	Journal	40	Exp-contr	Music Tx	0.45
Winter, et al.	1994	Surgery	Journal	50	Exp-contr	M.L.	0.44
Ashida	2000	Alzheimer's	Journal	20	Within Ss	Active music	0.44
Clark, et al.	1981	OB/GYN	Journal	20	Exp-contr	Music Tx	0.44
Liebman & MacLaren	1991	OB/GYN	Journal	39	Exp-contr	Music relax.	0.42
Mok & Wong	2003	Surgery	Journal	80	Exp-contr	M.L.	0.42
Ezzone, et al.	1998	Cancer/Term. Ill/HIV	Journal	33	Exp-contr	M.L.	0.42
Bolwerk	1990	Cardiology/ICU	Journal	40	Exp-contr	M.L.	0.42
Rider	1985	Rehabilitation	Journal	23	Within Ss	M.L.	0.41
Palakanis, et al.	1994	General Hospital	Journal	50	Exp-contr	M.L.	0.40
Davila & Menendez	1986	Dentistry	Journal	24	Within Ss	M.L.	0.40
Stein	1991	OB/GYN	Chapter	20	Exp-contr	M.L.	0.40
Thaut	1985	Rehabilitation	Journal	24	Exp-contr	M.L.	0.40
Thaut, et al.	1995	Rehabilitation	Journal	30	Exp-contr	M.L. (RAS)	0.40
Thaut, et al.	2002	Rehabilitation	Journal	21	Exp-contr	M.L. (RAS)	0.37
Yung, et al.	2003	Surgery	Journal	66	Exp-contr	M.L.	0.37
Hanser & Thompson	1994	Alzheimer's	Journal	30	Exp-contr	M.L.	0.36
Beck	1991	Cancer/Term. Ill/HIV	Journal	15	Within Ss	M.L.	0.36
White	1992	Cardiology/ICU	Journal	40	Exp-contr	M.L.	0.35
Barrera, et al.	2002	Cancer/Term. Ill/HIV	Journal	65	Within Ss	Active music	0.35

Good & Chin	1998	Surgery	Journal	38	Exp-contr	M.L.	0.34
Koch, et al.	1998	Surgery	Journal	40	Exp-contr	M.L.	0.34
Smith	1986	Alzheimer's	Journal	12	Within Ss	Music Tx	0.34
Burns, et al. (STUDY 1)	2001	Cancer/Term. Ill/HIV	Journal	18	Exp-contr	M.L.	0.34
Redmond	1985	Fetal	Dissert.	34	Within Ss	M.L.	0.34
Collins & Kuck	1991	Neo	Journal	16	Within Ss	M.L.	0.34
Pollack & Namazi	1992	Alzheimer's	Journal	8	Within Ss	Active music	0.33
McIntosh, et al.	1997	Rehabilitation	Journal	21	Exp-contr	M.L. (RAS)	0.32
Groene	1993	Alzheimer's	Dissert.	30	Within Ss	Active music	0.32
Steelman	1990	Surgery	Journal	28	Exp-contr	M.L.	0.32
Hurt, et al. (STUDY 2)	1998	Rehabilitation	Journal	5	Within Ss	M.L. (RAS)	0.32
Cassileth, et al.	2003	Cancer/Term. Ill/HIV	Journal	62	Exp-contr	Music Tx	0.30
White	1999	Cardiology/ ICU	Journal	30	Exp-contr	M.L.	0.30
VanderArk, et al.	1983	Alzheimer's	Journal	43	Exp-contr	Active music	0.30
Thaut, et al.	1997	Rehabilitation	Journal	20	Exp-contr	M.L. (RAS)	0.30
Coleman, et al.	1998	Neonatology	Journal	66	Exp-contr	M.L.	0.29
Clair	1994	Alzheimer's	Journal	28	Exp-contr	M.L.	0.29
Tang, et al.	1993	Surgery	Journal	120	Exp-contr	M.L.	0.29
Chlan	1995	Cardiology/ ICU	Journal	20	Exp-contr	M.L.	0.29
Haun, et al.	2001	Surgery	Journal	20	Exp-contr	M.L.	0.29
Lane	1989	Cancer/Term. Ill/HIV	Chapter	38	Exp-contr	M.L.	0.28
Macdonald, et al. (STUDY 1)	2003	Surgery	Journal	40	Exp-contr	M.L.	0.27
Dubois, et al.	1995	General Hospital	Journal	52	Exp-contr	M.L.	0.26
Schuster	1985	General Hospital	Journal	63	Exp-contr	M.L.	0.25
Metzler & Berman	1991	General Hospital	Journal	31	Exp-contr	M.L.	0.23
Renzi, et al.	2000	Surgery	Journal	86	Exp-contr	Music Imag.	0.23
Tusek, et al.	1997	Surgery	Journal	130	Exp-contr	Music Imag.	0.23
Cohen & Masse	1993	Rehabilitation	Journal	32	Exp-contr	Music Tx	0.21
Daub & Kirschner-Hermanns	1988	Surgery	Journal	60	Exp-contr	M.L.	0.21
Seukeran & Vestey	1997	Surgery	Paper	114	Exp-contr	M.L.	0.21
Nilsson, et al.	2001	Surgery	Journal	58	Exp-contr	M.L.	0.20
Kumar, et al.	1999	Alzheimer's	Journal	13	Within Ss	Music Tx	0.20

Chetta	1981	Surgery	Journal	75	Exp-contr	Active Music	0.20
Strauser	1997	Rehabilitation	Journal	27	Exp-contr	M.L.	0.19
Goff, et al.	1997	Dentistry	Journal	80	Exp-contr	M.L.	0.19
Fowler & Lander	1987	Pediatrics	Journal	20	Exp-contr	M.L.	0.19
Schwartz, et al.	1998	Neonatology	Chapter	67	Exp-contr	M.L.	0.18
Barnason, et al	1995	Surgery	Journal	64	Exp-Contr	M.L.	0.18
Caine	1991	Neonatology	Journal	52	Exp-contr	M.L.	0.18
Augustin & Hains	1996	Surgery	Journal	42	Exp-contr	M.L.	0.18
Hilliard	2003	Cancer/Term. Ill/HIV	Journal	80	Exp-contr	Music Tx	0.18
Moss	1987	Surgery	Journal	17	Exp-contr	M.L.	0.17
Lininger	1987	Neonatology	Thesis	36	Exp-contr	M.L.	0.16
Robb, et al.	1995	Surgery	Journal	20	Exp-contr	Music Relax.	0.16
Zimmerman, et al.	1996	Surgery	Journal	64	Exp-contr	M.L.	0.16
Calovini	1993	Cancer/Term. Ill/HIV	Thesis	11	Within Ss	Music Tx	0.15
Laurion & Fetzer	2002	Surgery	Journal	86	Exp-contr	M.L.	0.14
Lane	1991	Pediatrics	Dissert.	40	Exp-contr	Music Tx	0.14
Cassidy & Standley	1995	Neonatology	Journal	20	Within Ss	M.L.	0.14
Cadigan, et al.	2001	Cardiology/ICU	Journal	140	Exp-contr	M.L.	0.14
Haythornwaite, et al.	2001	Rehabilitation	Journal	42	Exp-contr	M.L.	0.13
Schneider, et al.	2001	General Hospital	Journal	30	Exp-contr	M.L.	0.13
Sohi	1997	Surgery	Dissert.	18	Exp-contr	Music Imag.	0.12
Kaempf & Amodie	1989	Surgery	Journal	33	Exp-contr	M.L.	0.11
Shapiro & Cohen	1986	OB/GYN	Chapter	500	Exp-contr	M.L.	0.11
Gaberson	1991	Surgery	Journal	31	Exp-contr	M.L.	0.10
Albert	2001	General Hospital	Dissert.	84	Exp-contr	Music Imag.	0.10
Burns, et al. (STUDY 2)	2001	Cancer/Term. Ill/HIV	Journal	18	Exp-contr	Active Music	0.09
Holstein	2000	Cardiology/ICU	Thesis	45	Within Ss	M.L.	0.09
Wang, et al.	2002	Surgery	Journal	93	Within-Ss	M.L.	0.09
Hamel	2001	Cardiology/ICU	Journal	101	Exp-contr	M.L.	0.08
Blankfield, et al.	1995	Surgery	Journal	61	Exp-contr	M.L.	0.07
Mandle et al.	1990	General Hospital	Journal	30	Exp-contr	M.L.	0.07
Tanioka	1987	Surgery	Chapter	30	Exp-contr	M.L.	0.07

Winter, et al.	1994	Surgery	Journal	31	Exp-contr	M.L.	0.06
Cepeda, et al.	1998	General Hospital	Journal	193	Exp-contr	M.L.	0.05
Sabo & Michael	1996	Cancer/Term. Ill/HIV	Journal	97	Exp-contr	M.L.	0.05
Jacobson	1999	General Hospital	Journal	72	Exp-contr	M.L.	0.05
Smith, et al.	2001	Cancer/Term. Ill/HIV	Journal	42	Exp-contr	M.L.	0.05
Good et al.	2002	Surgery	Journal	65	Exp-contr	M.L.	0.04
Evans & Rubio	1994	Surgery	Journal	24	Exp-contr	M.L.	0.03
Reilly	1999	Surgery	Dissert.	31	Exp-contr	M.L.	0.02
Macdonald, et al. (STUDY 2)	2003	Surgery	Journal	58	Exp-contr	M.L.	0.00
Heitz	1992	Surgery	Journal	60	Exp-contr	M.L.	0.00
Davis	1992	OB/GYN	Journal	22	Exp-contr	M.L.	0.00
Zimmerman, et al.	1988	Cardiology/ ICU	Journal	75	Exp-contr	M.L.	0.00
Heiser, et al.	1997	Surgery	Journal	10	Exp-contr	M.L.	0.00
Tibbs	1991	Pediatrics	Thesis	30	Exp-contr	M.L.	0.00
Ryan	1989	Pediatrics	Chapter	14	Exp-contr	M.L.	0.00
Elliott	1994	Cardiology/ ICU	Journal	56	Exp-contr	M.L.	0.00
Arts, et al.	1994	Surgery	Journal	180	Exp-contr	M.L.	0.00
Lepage, et al.	2001	Surgery	Journal	50	Exp-contr	M.L.	0.00
Davis-Rollans & Cunningham	1987	Cardiology/ ICU	Journal	24	Within Ss	M.L.	0.00
Elche & Lavelle	1998	Pediatrics	Dissert.	25	Exp-contr	M.L.	0.00
Durham & Collins	1986	OB/GYN	Journal	30	Exp-contr	M.L.	0.00
Aitken, et al.	2002	Dentistry	Journal	45	Exp-contr	M.L.	0.00
Standley	1991	Neonatology	Journal	33	Exp-contr	M.L.	0.00
Silber	1999	Alzheimer's	Journal	18	Exp-contr	M.L.	0.00
Colt, et al.	1999	General Hospital	Journal	60	Exp-contr	M.L.	0.00
Cordobes	1997	Cancer/Term. Ill/HIV	Journal	18	Exp-contr	Active Music	0.00
Menegazzi, et al.	1991	General Hospital	Journal	38	Exp-contr	M.L.	0.00
Owens	1979	Neonatology	Journal	59	Exp-contr	M.L.	0.00
Curtis	1986	Cancer/Term. Ill/HIV	Journal	9	Within Ss	M.L.	0.00
Whittal	1989	Cancer/Term. Ill/HIV	Chapter	16	Within Ss	Music Tx	0.00
Cohen & Ford	1995	Rehabilitation	Journal	12	Within Ss	Active music	0.00
Howitt & Stricker	1966	Dentistry	Journal	46	Exp-contr	M.L.	0.00
Malloy	1979	Neonatology	Chapter	127	Exp-contr	M.L.	0.00

Cruise, et al	1997	Surgery	Journal	61	Exp-contr	M.L.	0.00
Corah, et al.	1981	Dentistry	Journal	80	Exp-contr	M.L.	0.00
Chapman	1979	Neonatology	Chapter	153	Exp-contr	M.L.	0.00
Chapman	1978	Neonatology	Journal	153	Exp-contr	M.L.	0.00
Abbott	1995	Cancer/Term. Ill/HIV	Thesis	28	Exp-contr	Music Tx	0.00
Good	1995	Surgery	Journal	21	Exp-contr	M.L.	0.00
Taylor, et al.	1998	Surgery	Journal	61	Exp-contr	M.L.	0.00
Schinner et al.	1995	Rehabilitation	Journal	15	Within Ss	M.L.	0.00
Burke	1997	Surgery	Chapter	20	Exp-contr	M.L.	0.00
Broscious	1999	Surgery	Journal	103	Exp-contr	M.L.	0.00
Hurt, et al. (STUDY 1)	1998	Rehabilitation	Journal	8	Within Ss	M.L. (RAS)	0.00
Kliempt, et al.	1999	Surgery	Journal	50	Exp-contr	M.L.	-0.08
Elm, et al.	1998	Alzheimer's	Journal	30	Within Ss	M.L.	-0.20

[1] M.L. : Music listening
Music Tx: Music therapy session with a variety of music therapy techniques
Music Imag.: Music and imagery
Music Relax. Music and relaxation
Active Music: Active music making by patients

Table 11 provides mean sample-level effect sizes. First, the overall mean sample-level effect size for the 183 studies included in this review was computed. This resulted in a significant $r = .31$, or a moderate effect size overall. However, because studies using a variety of interventions and examining a variety of outcome measures were combined in one large analysis, a significant Q-value was found, indicating that the effect sizes were inconsistent across studies. This was predicted given the range of studies included.

In addition, a mean sample-level effect size for each of the 11 medical specialties was computed. All effect sizes were statistically significant, except for the mean sample-level effect size for dentistry studies. According to the interpretation guidelines provided by Cohen (1977), a small, but significant effect size was found for three medical specializations (Cardiology/ICU, General Hospital, and Neonatology). Three medical specializations (Surgery, OB/GYN and Cancer/Terminal Illness/HIV), approached values that are considered moderate ($r = .25$). For Pediatrics and Rehabilitation, the sample-level effect size was significant and considered moderate. Moreover, studies related to Fetal responses and studies in Alzheimer's disease resulted in a large mean effect size. For four specializations, the homogeneity statistic Q was significant, even after exclusion of outliers, meaning that the effect sizes were inconsistent across studies. This was, expected as the studies examined different independent and dependent variables.

23

Table 11
Sample-Level Effect Sizes

Medical Specialty	k	N	r_u	95% c.i.	p	Q
Across medical specialties	183	7894	.31	+.26 to +.35	.00	640.48*
Across medical specialties. (outliers removed)[1]	180	7794	.29	+.25 to +.33	.00	469.34*
Surgery	51	2779	.26	+.18 to +.35	.00	246.86*
Surgery (outliers removed)[2]	49	2689	.22	+.16 to +.28	.00	114.23*
Cardiology/ICU	14	666	.27	+.14 to +.40	.00	36.50*
Cardiology/ICU (outlier removed)[3]	13	631	.21	+.10 to +.31	.00	20.36
Cancer/Terminal Illness/HIV	18	641	.22	+.14 to +.30	.00	16.81
Fetal	4	81	.57	+.34 to +.74	.00	4.31
General Hospital	11	703	.12	+.05 to +.19	.00	9.67
Neonatology	17	895	.21	+.10 to +.32	.00	35.63*
OB/GYN	7	638	.23	+.06 to +.39	.01	10.59
Pediatrics	11	291	.39	+.20 to +.56	.00	29.60*
Pediatrics (outlier removed)[4]	10	271	.34	+.15 to +.51	.00	22.44*
Dentistry	6	311	.16	-.01 to +.32	.06	9.92
Alzheimer's	26	547	.56	+.42 to +.67	.00	89.75*
Alzheimer's (outliers removed)[5]	23	479	.57	+.47 to +.67	.00	46.54
Rehabilitation	18	372	.38	+.25 to +.49	.00	22.67

[1] Allen, Golden, Izzo, et al. (2001), $r = .97$; Brotons & Pickett-Cooper (1996), $r = .93$; Kliempt, Ruta, Ogston, Landeck & Martay (1999), $r = -.08$; Elm, Madill, & Warren (1998), $r = -.20$
[2] Allen et al. (2001), $r = .97$; Kliempt et al. (1999), $r = -.08$
[3] Chlan (1998), $r = .72$
[4] Ammon (1963), $r = .78$
[5] Elm, Madill, & Warren (1998), $r = -.20$; Silber (1999), $r = .00$; Brotons & Pickett-Cooper (1996), $r = .93$
* $p < .05$, indicating that the sample is not homogeneous.

Moderator Analyses for Mean Sample-Level Effect Sizes

Across medical specializations. After the exclusion of 4 outliers, the overall mean sample-level effect size, $r = .29$, remained associated with excess variability. Moderator analyses resulted in some interesting findings (Table 12). The type of intervention and category of intervention were both found to be moderator variables. Active music making and music therapy sessions with a variety of interventions achieved the highest mean effect sizes. Moreover, the data suggested that music therapy studies were significantly more effective than music medicine studies. The level of randomization also functioned as a moderator variable with within-subjects designs leading to the highest effect sizes.

Table 12
Moderator Analysis for Mean Sample-Level Effect Size
(Across Specializations)

Categorical Variable	Moderator						
Medical Specialty	No						
Type of Intervention	Yes						
	k	r_u	95% c.i.	p	$Q_b{}^*$	v^{**}	
Music Listening	137	.26	+.22 to +.30	.00	13.65	$v = .04$	
Music and Imagery	5	.22	+.002 to +.42	.05	$(p = .01)$	se(v)=	
Active Music Making	16	.50	+.38 to +.61	.00		.01	
Mixed Music Therapy Techniques	19	.35	+.23 to +.46	.00			
Music and Relaxation	2	.32	-.06 to +.62	.10			
Category of Intervention	Yes						
	k	r_u	95% c.i.	p	$Q_b{}^*$	v	
Music Medicine	120	.24	+.20 to +.28	.00	15.35	$v = .04$	
Music Therapy	59	.40	+.34 to +.47	.00	$(p = .00)$	se(v)= .01	
Patient Music Preference	No						
Preferred	75	.28	+.23 to +.34	.00	1.11	$v = .03$	
Non-preferred	73	.24	+.18 to +.30	.00	$(p = .29)$	se(v)= .01	
Level of Randomization	Yes						
Randomized	90	.24	+.19 to +.28	.00	30.63	$v = .03$	
Non-Randomized	24	.30	+.20 to +.39	.00	$(p = .00)$	se(v)= .01	
Within-Ss	51	.47	+.40 to +.54	.00			
Unknown	14	.15	+.02 to +.27	.02			

*Q_b is the between-category variance. The categorical variable is considered a moderator variable when p≤ .05
** v and $se(v)$ is the random effects variance component and its standard error. If v is zero, the moderator variable accounts for all excess variability.

To ascertain that the higher effect size for music therapy studies was not due to level of randomization, a separate moderator analysis was run for level of randomization for music therapy studies versus music medicine studies (Table 13). This analysis suggested that music therapy interventions were indeed more effective than music medicine interventions and that this difference was not due to differences in level of randomization. Music preference did not act as a moderator variable for the overall mean sample-level effect size.

Table 13
Moderator Analysis for Level of Randomization According to
Category of Intervention

Level of Randomization	k	r_u	95% c.i.	p	Q_b
Music Medicine Studies					
Randomized	74	.22	+.16 to +.28	.00	9.92
Non-Randomized	16	.34	+.19 to +.48	.00	(p=.02)
Within-Ss	25	.42	+.30 to +.52	.00	
Unknown	13	.16	+.00 to +.31	.04	
Music Therapy Studies					
Randomized	18	.43	+.30 to +.53	.00	6.89
Non-Randomized	8	.26	+.04 to +.45	.02	(p = .03)
Within-Ss	28	.54	+.43 to +.64	.00	

Surgery. The mean sample-level effect size for surgery studies, $r = .26$, was associated with a significant Q-value (heterogeneity). The exclusion of two outliers did not result in a homogeneous distribution of effect sizes. Music listening $(k=46)$ was the main intervention used in this medical specialization. In addition, three studies used music and imagery, one used active music-making, and one study used a variety of music therapy techniques.

Because of the predominance of music listening interventions, no meaningful moderator analysis could be conducted for the type of intervention. Studies that used patient-preferred music yielded a higher mean effect size than studies that did not take music preference into account. However, this difference was not statistically significant (Table 14).

Because 49 studies were categorized as music medicine and only two studies were considered music therapy, the category of intervention could not be analyzed as a moderator variable. Finally, the level of randomization was not found to be a moderator variable. Of the 51 studies, 39 used randomization, five were non- randomized, and two used within-subject designs. In five of the studies, the level of randomization was not specified.

Table 14
Moderator Analysis for Mean Sample-Level Effect Size (Surgery)

Categorical Variable	Moderator					
Medical Specialty	N/A					
Type of Intervention	No					
Category of Intervention	No					
	k	r_u	95% c.i.	p	Q_b	v
Music Medicine	49		N/A			
Music Therapy	2					
Music Preference	No					
Preferred	34	.31	+.21 to +.41	.00	3.12	$v = .085$
Non-preferred	17	.15	-.01 to +.30	.07	($p = .07$)	se(v)=.02
Level of Randomization	No					

Cardiology/ICU. All studies in the cardiology/ICU medical specialization used music listening as the experimental condition; 6 studies used patient-preferred music. All studies were categorized as music medicine. Although the use of patient-preferred music resulted in a higher effect size ($r = .36$) compared to non-preferred music ($r = .21$), this did not function as a moderator variable nor did any of the other categorical variables. Eight studies in this medical specialization used randomized, two used non-randomized, and four used within-subjects designs.

Cancer/Terminal Illness/HIV. For this medical specialization the Q statistic for the mean sample level effect size suggested a homogeneous distribution of effect sizes. Nine studies used music listening, one used music and imagery, one used active music therapy, and five used music therapy sessions with a variety of music therapy techniques. Of the 9 studies using music listening, 8 used patient-preferred music. Eight studies were classified as music medicine, and 10 were classified as music therapy. The music medicine studies resulted in a mean effect size of $r=.25$ and the music therapy studies in a mean effect size of $r = .20$, but this difference was not statistically significant. Four studies used a randomized designed, 6 a non-randomized designs and 7 a within-subjects design. For one study, the level of randomization was unknown.

Fetal. Only 4 studies were included in this category. The Q-statistic indicated a homogeneous distribution of the effect sizes. All studies involved music listening and were classified as music medicine. One study used randomized sampling, and the other three studies used a within-subjects design. Because of the small number of studies and the distribution of the studies for each categorical variable, no moderator analyses could be conducted.

General Hospital. The effect size distribution of these 11 studies was found to be homogeneous. Ten studies investigated music listening, and one study music and imagery; only 5 studies used patient-preferred music. All studies were classified as music medicine. Nine studies used randomized experiments, and two studies were non-randomized. Because of the small k, no moderator variables could be identified in the analysis.

Neonatology. All 17 studies used music listening and, because of the non-verbal status of the patients, preference was not a consideration in this population. Five studies were randomized, three were non-randomized, and seven used a within-subject design. For two studies, the level of randomization was unknown. In addition, 11 studies were classified as music medicine, and 6 were considered music therapy; however, the category of intervention did not function as a moderator variable.

Level of randomization acted as an important moderator variable. As shown in table 15, the within-subject study designs yielded a much larger mean effect size than the randomized and the non-randomized designs. Because of the value of the variance component ($v = .00$), it can be concluded that all excess variability can be explained by the level of randomization.

Table 15
Moderator Analysis for Mean Sample-Level Effect Size (Neonatology)

Categorical Variable	Moderator					
Medical Specialty	N/A					
Type of Intervention	N/A					
Category of Intervention	No					
	k	r_u	95% c.i.	p	Q_b	v
Music Medicine	11	.21	+.08 to +.33	.00	.00	$v = .03$
Music Therapy	6	.20	+.01 to +.39	.04	(p = .96)	(se)v =.02
Music Preference	N/A					
Level of Randomization	Yes					
Randomized	5	.08	-.01 to +.18	.09	21.01	$v = .00$
Non-Randomized	3	.12	-.03 to +.27	.11	(p =	se(v)=.00
Within-Ss	7	.49	+.33 to +.62	.00	.00)	
Unknown	2	.00	-.16 to +.16	1.00		

OB/GYN. The Q-test indicated that the effect sizes of these 7 studies were homogeneous. Even though a non-significant Q-value was found for this group of studies, a mixed effects model was fitted to the data because of the low level of effect sizes.

Interestingly, the category of intervention seemed to significantly alter the results in this medical specialization. Those studies that used music therapy interventions resulted in a much higher effect size than those using music medicine treatment, and this difference was statistically significant (Table 16). Four studies examined music listening, one study used music listening and imagery, and two studies used a variety of music therapy interventions, but type of intervention did not function as a moderator variable. Two studies used randomized, three used non-randomized sampling, and one study used a within-subjects design. For one study, the level of randomization was not specified, however, level of randomization did not act as a moderator variable.

Table 16
Moderator Analysis for Mean Sample-Level Effect Size (OB/GYN)

Categorical Variable	Moderator						
Medical Specialty	N/A						
Type of Intervention	No						
Category of Intervention	Yes						
		k	r_u	95% c.i.	p	Q_b	v
Music Medicine		5	.13	+.05 to +.21	.00	3.79	$v = .00$
Music Therapy		2	.51	+.13 to +.76	.01	(p = .05)	se(v)= .00
Music Preference	No						
Preferred		6		N/A			
Non-preferred		1					
Level of Randomization	No						

Pediatrics. The effect sizes for this population group were inconsistent across studies. Even after the removal of one outlier, heterogeneity remained. The data suggested that music therapy interventions were more effective than music medicine interventions, and this difference was significant (Table 17). The music therapy studies used a variety of music therapy interventions within the experimental session, and the music medicine studies used music listening. The level of randomization was not found to be a moderator variable. Eight studies used randomized, and two used non-randomized sampling; one study used a within-subjects design.

Dentistry. All 6 dentistry studies used music listening as the experimental intervention and were classified as music medicine. No differences in effect sizes were found between the use of preferred ($k = 3$) and non-preferred ($k = 3$) music. The Q-statistic indicated a homogeneous distribution of the effect sizes. Subsequent analysis was unable to identify any significant moderator variables. Four studies used randomized, and one study non-randomized sampling. One study used a within-subjects design.

Table 17
Moderator Analysis for Mean Sample-Level Effect Size (Pediatrics)

Categorical Variable	Moderator						
Medical Specialty	N/A						
Type of Intervention	Yes[1]						
Category of Intervention	Yes						
	k	r_u	95% c.i.	p	Q_b	v	
Music Medicine	5	.13	-.11 to +.35	.23	6.67	$v = .02$	
Music Therapy	5	.49	+.32 to +.63	.00	(p = .01)	se(v)= .04	
Music Preference	No						
Preferred	3		N/A				
Non-preferred	1						
Level of Randomization	No						

[1] Same statistics as 'Category of Intervention'

Alzheimer's. Within this medical specialization, different music therapy interventions (music listening, active music making, and music therapy sessions with a variety of techniques) resulted in different mean effect sizes ($r = .48$, $r = .58$, and $r = .67$, respectively). However, these differences were not statistically significant. Twenty-one studies were classified as music therapy, and 5 studies were classified as music medicine. It is important to note that the variability of effect sizes was large in the music medicine studies, but not in the music therapy studies (Table 18).

Table 18
Moderator Analysis for Mean Sample-Level Effect Size (Alzheimer's)

Categorical Variable	Moderator						
Medical Specialty	N/A						
Type of Intervention	No						
Category of Intervention	No						
	k	r_u	95% c.i.	p	Q_b	v	
Music Medicine	5	.35	+.02 to +.61	.04	2.73	$v = .11$	
Music Therapy	21	.60	+.47 to +.71	.01	(p = .10)	se(v)= .05	
Music Preference	No						
Preferred	5	.64	+.45 to +.78	.00	.80	$v = .03$	
Non-preferred	4	.53	+.30 to +.70	.00	(p = .37)	se(v)= .04	
Level of Randomization	No						

This implies that music therapy interventions led to more consistent results than music listening. Because most studies in this medical specialization involved music therapy (beyond music listening), music preference was not relevant as a moderator variable. Level of randomization was also not found to be a moderator variable: 3 studies used a randomized experimental design, two used a non-randomized design, and 19 studies used a within-subject design. For one study, the level of randomization was unknown.

Rehabilitation. The Q-value indicated a homogeneous distribution of sample-level effect sizes for this medical specialization. Thirteen studies used music listening, including rhythmic auditory stimulation, whereas three studies used active music making, and two studies used a variety of music therapy experiences. All interventions led to similar mean sample-level effect sizes, namely .36 (p = .00), .43 (p = .01), and .38 (p = .03) respectively. The difference between these mean effect sizes was not statistically significant. Four studies were classified as music medicine, and 14 studies as music therapy. This categorical variable was not found to be a moderator variable. The use of patient-preferred music vs. non-preferred music did not appear to make a difference within this specialization (Table 19). Ten studies used randomized sampling, and eight studies used a within-subject design. Although the within-subject designs led to higher effect sizes (.49 compared to .32), this difference was not statistically significant.

Table 19
Moderator Analysis for Mean Sample-Level Effect Size (Rehabilitation)

Categorical Variable	Moderator						
Medical Specialty	N/A						
Type of Intervention	No						
Category of Intervention	No						
	k	r_u	95% c.i.	p	Q_b	v	
Music Medicine	4	.33	+.10 to +.52	.00	.28	v = .02	
Music Therapy	14	.40	+.23 to +.52	.00	(p = .59)	se(v)= .02	
Music Preference	No						
Preferred	6	.35	+.16 to +.52	.00	.00	v = .02	
Non-preferred	9	.35	+.16 to +.51	.00	(p = .96)	se(v)= .03	
Level of Randomization	No						

In this section, effect sizes for specific outcome measures (dependent variables) are described. For each symptom or outcome measure, the mean effect size across medical specialization as well as the mean effect size per specialization is listed. When only one study was available within a specialization, the symptom-level effect size for that study is listed, however no mean effect size with a confidence interval could be calculated. When only a few studies (< 5) could be included for a specific variable, the confidence interval was likely to include zero, indicating that the effect size was non-significant. It is important to note that this does **not** mean that all studies reported non-significant findings. Rather, this reflects that more studies (and a larger sample size) are needed to demonstrate that the treatment intervention is more effective than the control condition.

Finally, as stated previously, a significant Q statistic ($p \leq .05$) indicates that the findings are inconsistent across studies. When this occurred, outliers were removed, and moderator variable analyses were conducted in an attempt to identify categorical variables that could serve as the source of the excess variability. Therefore, for each outcome measure, there is an indication of the influence/lack of influence of the following moderator variables: (a) medical specialization, (b) type of intervention, (c) category of intervention, (d) music preference, and (e) level of randomization. In addition, comparison data between music medicine and music therapy studies are provided. Finally, comparison data for studies using patient-preferred music and studies not using patient-preferred music are given. At times, these comparisons may not be meaningful because of the disproportionate numbers of studies in various categories. For example, for the outcome measure 'heart rate,' 39 studies were classified as music medicine, whereas only 3 studies were identified as music therapy; comparisons of these interventions, therefore would not provide meaningful data.

Heart Rate

Mean effect size. Many studies ($k = 44$) examined the effects of music on patients' heart rates, resulting in a mean effect size of $r = .24$ after removal of two outliers. However, this effect size remained associated with a heterogeneous distribution of effect sizes across populations (Table 20). Studies in neonatology obtained the largest, statistically significant mean effect size ($r = .30$). Two studies examining the effect of music on fetal heart rate resulted in a high mean effect size ($r = .57$). This effect size approached statistical significance, however more studies and larger sample sizes are needed to validate this effect.

Moderator analysis. Three medical specializations had a heterogeneous distribution of effect sizes for heart rate: Surgery, Cardiology/ICU and General Hospital. The distribution of the effect sizes across populations was also found to be heterogeneous. In an attempt to identify moderator variables, a mixed effects model was fitted to the data (Tables 21-23). No meaningful moderator analyses

32

could be conducted for General Hospital because of the limited number of studies (k= 4).

Table 20
Mean Effect Sizes for Heart Rate

Medical Specialty	k	N	r_u	95% c.i.	p	Q
Across specializations	44	1883	.28	+.17 to + .40	.00	239.75*
Across specializations (outliers removed)[1]	42	1805	.24	+.15 to + .32	.00	138.93*
Surgery	16	803	.34	+.12 to + .53	.00	153.68*
Surgery (outlier removed)[2]	15	763	.24	+.07 to + .38	.00	63.93*
Cardiology/ICU	12	606	.21	+.05 to + .36	.00	39.86*
Cardiology/ICU (outliers removed)[3]	11	579	.13	.00 to + .25	.04	18.76*
Cancer/HIV	2	27	.17	- .26 to + .53	.45	.94
Fetal	2	45	.57	- .04 to + .68	.07	3.27
General Hospital[4]	4	111	.25	- .14 to + .57	.21	16.36*
Neonatology	5	140	.30	+.09 to + .49	.01	5.56
Dentistry	2	91	.00	- .21 to +. 21	1.0	.00
OB/GYN	1	22	.00			

[1] Allen, Golden, Izzo, et al. (2001), r = .95; Menegazzi, Paris, Kersteen, Flynn, & Trautman (1991),
r = -.13
[2] Allen, Golden, Izzo, et al. (2001), r = .95
[3] Chlan (1998), r = .78
[4] No outliers
* p<.05, indicating that the sample is not homogeneous.

Table 21
Moderator Analysis for Heart Rate (Across Specializations)

Categorical Variable	Moderator					
Medical Specialty	No					
Type of Intervention	No					
Category of Intervention	No					
	k	r_u	95% c.i.	p	Q_b	v
Music Medicine	38	.25	+.16 to +.34	.00	.86	v = .06
Music Therapy	4	.08	-.27 to +.41	.66	(p= .35)	(se)v = .02
Music Preference	No					
Preferred	17	.33	+.20 to +.44	.00	3.23	v = .05
Non-preferred	23	.17	+.05 to +.28	.01	(p =.07)	se(v) = .02
Level of Randomization	No					

Table 22
Moderator Analysis for Heart Rate (Surgery)

Categorical Variable	Moderator					
Medical Specialty	N/A					
Type of Intervention	No					
Category of Intervention	No					
	k	r_u	95% c.i.	p	Q_b	v
Music Medicine	14	.24	+.09 to +.39	.00	N/A	N/A
Music Therapy	1	.00	N/A	N/A		
Music Preference	Yes					
Preferred	10	.32	+.16 to +.46	.00	3.91	v = .05
Non-preferred	5	.02	-.22 to +.27	.86	(p = .05)	se(v) = .03
Level of Randomization	No					

Table 23
Moderator Analysis for Heart Rate (Cardiology/ICU)

Categorical Variable	Moderator					
Medical Specialty	N/A					
Type of Intervention	No					
Category of Intervention	No					
	k	r_u	95% c.i.	p	Q_b	v
Music Medicine	11	.13	.00 to +.25	.04	N/A	N/A
Music Therapy	0					
Music Preference	No					
Preferred	4	.21	+.04 to +.37	.02	2.24	v = .01
Non-preferred	7	.05	-.06 to +.17	.37	(p = .13)	se(v)= .00
Level of Randomization	Yes					
Random	6	.03	-.06 to +.12	.54	6.23	v = .00
Non-Random	2	.25	-.08 to +.53	.14	(p =.04)	se(v)= .00
Within-Ss	3	.29	+.09 to +.47	.01		.00

Respiration Rate

Mean effect size. A mean effect size of r = .26 was obtained across specializations after exclusion of one outlier. However, a heterogeneous distribution of effect sizes was present. Significant small to moderate effect sizes were obtained for surgery and cardiology/ICU (Table 24). These effect sizes were homogeneous. Unfortunately, few studies examined respiration rate as a dependent variable in other medical specializations.

Moderator analysis. After the removal of outliers, homogeneity was reached for all individual specializations. A moderator analysis was conducted for the effect size across specializations, as this remained associated with heterogeneity (Table 25). Even though no statistical significance was reached for the categorical variable of 'specialization' ($p = .07$), the data suggest that the medical specialty group had some influence on the distribution of the effect sizes. No other moderator variables were found.

Table 24
Mean Effect Size for Respiration Rate

Medical Specialty	k	N	r_u	95% c.i.	p	Q
Across specializations	22	738	.32	+.18 to +.44	.00	75.70*
Across specializations (outlier removed)[1]	21	731	.26	+.15 to +.36	.00	38.11*
Surgery	6	241	.19	+.06 to +.31	.00	4.82
Cardiology/ICU	7	301	.50	+.21 to +.71	.00	39.74*
Cardiology/ICU (outliers removed)[2]	5	274	.37	+.22 to +.51	.00	5.51
Neonatology	2	44	.22	-.18 to +.55	.29	1.59
General Hospital	2	69	.06	-.18 to +.30	.63	.19
Rehabilitation	1	31	.00			
OB/GYN	1	22	.00			
Pediatrics	1	25	.00			
Cancer/Terminal Illness/HIV	1	16	.00			
Fetal	1	20	.66			

[1] Chlan (1998), $r = .91$
[2] Chlan (1998), $r = .91$; Davis-Rollans & Cunningham (1987), $r = .00$
* p<.05, indicating that the sample is not homogeneous.

Table 25
Moderator Analysis for Respiration Rate (Across Specializations)

Categorical Variable	Moderator						
Medical Specialty	No						
Type of Intervention	No						
Category of Intervention	No						
	k	r_u	95% c.i.	p	Q_b	v	
Music Medicine	18	.28	+.18 to +.38	.00	2.80	v = 02	
Music Therapy	3	.00	-.31 to +.31	1.00	(p= .09)	se(v)=.02	
Music Preference	No						
Preferred	7	.26	+.08 to +.42	.01	.02	v = .03	
Non-preferred	15	.27	+.14 to +.39	.00	(p = .89)	se(v)=.02	
Level of Randomization	No						

Blood Pressure

Mean effect sizes. Results for the dependent variable, blood pressure, were reported in different ways in the studies in this meta-analysis. In the majority of studies, systolic and diastolic blood pressure results were reported separately. However, in 7 studies, no distinction was made between systolic and diastolic, and all results were reported under the general term, 'blood pressure.' In addition, 6 studies reported 'Mean Arterial Pressure' as the outcome variable. Therefore, the tables below are consistent with the study data, and information is provided separately on systolic blood pressure, diastolic blood pressure, mean arterial pressure, and 'blood pressure' in general.

Twenty-two studies examined the effects of music on diastolic blood pressure, four of which needed to be removed because of extreme values. This resulted in a small but significant mean effect size of $r = .18$. An initial analysis resulted in a mean effect size of $r = .44$ for the surgery specialization. However, after exclusion of two outliers, the mean effect size was calculated at $r = .23$. For cardiology/ICU, a small but significant mean effect size of $r = .10$ was obtained (Table 26). Similar results were obtained for systolic blood pressure (Table 27). Results for the outcome measure, 'blood pressure,' are listed in Table 28. Six studies measured the effects of music listening on mean arterial pressure. Across specializations, this resulted in a mean effect size of .66. However, the effect sizes were characterized by a heterogeneous distribution (Table 29). Removing two outliers resulted in a lower effect size ($r = .31$), but did not resolve the heterogeneity.

Table 26
Mean Effect Size for Diastolic Blood Pressure

Medical Specialty	k	N	r_u	95% c.i.	p	Q
Across Specializations	22	2028	.27	+.09 to + .42	.00	177.92*
Across specializations (outliers removed)[1]	18	1029	.18	+.09 to +.27	.00	34.96*
Surgery	11	541	.44	+.13 to + .67	.01	139.24*
Surgery (outliers removed)[2]	9	491	.23	+.08 to +.38	.00	21.96*
Cardiology/ICU	8	475	.10	+.01 to + .19	.04	5.27
General Hospital	2	101	.07	-.30 to +.42	.71	3.4
Cancer/Term.Ill./HIV	1	11	-.28			

[1]Calovini (1993), $r = -.28$; Menegazzi, Paris, Kersteen, Flynn, & Trautman (1991), $r = -.14$; Updike & Charles (1987), $r = .84$; Allen et al. (2001), $r = .97$
[2] Updike & Charles (1987), $r = .84$; Allen et al. (2001), $r = .97$
*p<.05, indicating that the sample is not homogeneous.

Table 27
Mean Effect Size for Systolic Blood Pressure

Medical Specialty	k	N	r_u	95% c.i.	p	Q
Across Specializations	25	1194	.28	+.10 to + .45	.00	222.88*
Across Specializations (outliers removed)[1]	21	1055	.19	+.11 to +.26	.00	27.62
Surgery	12	550	.44	+.10 to + .69	.01	190.82*
Surgery (outliers removed)[2]	9	450	.26	+.16 to +.35	.00	8.93
Cardiology/ICU	9	505	.12	+.001 to + .24	.05	12.61
General Hospital	2	101	.05	-.37 to +.44	.83	4.38*
Cancer/Term.Ill./HIV	1	11	.35			

[1] Kliempt, Ruta, Ogston, Landeck, & Martay (1999), $r = -.42$; Menegazzi et al. (1991), $r = -.19$; Updike & Charles (1987), $r = .90$; Allen et al. (2001), $r = .98$
[2] Kliempt et al (1999), $r = -.42$; Updike & Charles (1987), $r = .90$; Allen et al. (2001), $r = .98$
* p<.05, indicating that the sample is not homogeneous.

Table 28
Mean Effect Size for 'Blood Pressure'

Medical Specialty	k	N	r_u	95% c.i.	p	Q
Across Specializations[1]	7	332	.17	-.01 to + .35	.07	13.74*
Surgery	4	241	.03	-.10 to + .16	.61	2.55
General Hospital	2	61	.25	-.25 to + .64	.32	3.58
Cardiology/ICU	1	20	.58			

[1] No outliers
* p<.05, indicating that the sample is not homogeneous.

Table 29
Mean Effect Size for Mean Arterial Pressure

Medical Specialty	k	N	r_u	95% c.i.	p	Q
Across specializations	6	222	.66	+.29 to +.86	.00	58.74*
Across specializations (outliers removed)[1]	4	192	.31	+.06 to +.52	.02	8.54*
Surgery	3	136	.74	+.02 to +.95	.05	44.59*
General Hospital	1	50	.46			
Cardiology/ICU	1	20	.87			
Neonatology	1	16	.31			

[1] Updike (1990), $r = .87$; Updike & Charles (1987), $r = .99$

* $p<.05$, indicating that the sample is not homogeneous.

Moderator analysis. Tables 30 and 31 list the results for two mean effect sizes for diastolic blood pressure that were associated with a lack of homogeneity: the mean effect size across specializations and the surgery mean effect size. Homogeneity was obtained for the systolic blood pressure effect sizes. Group comparisons for category of intervention and for music preference are given for the across populations results in table 32. Table 33 lists results for moderator analysis for the outcome measure, 'blood pressure.' Applying a mixed effects model to the data for mean arterial pressure (across specializations) identified music preference as the main moderator variable (Table 34).

Table 30
Moderator Analysis for Diastolic Blood Pressure (Across Specializations)

Categorical Variable	Moderator						
Medical Specialty	No						
Type of Intervention	No						
Category of Intervention	No						
	k	r_u	95% c.i.	p	Q_b	v	
Music Medicine	18	.18	+.09 to +.27	.00	N/A	N/A	
Music Therapy	0						
Music Preference	Yes						
Preferred	11	.26	+.16 to +.35	.00	5.29	$v = .01$	
Non-preferred	7	.07	-.07 to +.20	.31	(p = .02)	se(v)=.01	
Level of Randomization	No						

Table 31
Moderator Analysis for Diastolic Blood Pressure (Surgery)

Categorical Variable	Moderator					
Medical Specialty	No					
Type of Intervention	No					
Category of Intervention	No					
	k	r_u	95% c.i.	p	Q_b	v
Music Medicine	9		N/A			
Music Therapy	0					
Music Preference	Yes					
Preferred	6	.33	+.20 to +.44	.00	6.16	v = .01
Non-preferred	3	.00	-.23 to +.23	1.00	(p = .01)	se(v)=.01
Level of Randomization	No					

Table 32
Moderator Analysis for Systolic Blood Pressure (Across Specializations)

Categorical Variable	Moderator					
Medical Specialty	No					
Type of Intervention	No					
Category of Intervention	No					
	k	r_u	95% c.i.	p	Q_b	v
Music Medicine	20		N/A			
Music Therapy	1					
Music Preference	No					
Preferred	13	.21	+.12 to +.30	.00	.76	v =.01
Non-preferred	7	.15	+.02 to +.26	.02	(p=.39)	se(v)=.01
Level of Randomization	No					

Table 33
Moderator Analysis for "Blood Pressure" (Across Specializations)

Categorical Variable	Moderator					
Medical Specialty	Yes					
	k	r_u	95% c.i.	p	Q_b	v
Surgery	4	.03	-.09 to +.16	.61	7.61	v = .00
Cardiology/ICU	1	.58	+.18 to +.81	.01	(p =.02)	se(v)=.0
General Hospital	2	.25	-.01 to +.47	.06		1
Category of Intervention	No					
	k	r_u	95% c.i.	p	Q_b	v
Music Medicine	6	N/A				
Music Therapy	1					
Music Preference	No					
Preferred	4	.15	-.06 to +.36	.15	.02	v = .02
Non-preferred	3	.18	-.11 to +.44	.21	(p = .88)	se(v)=.0 3
Level of Randomization	No					

Table 34
Moderator Analysis for Mean Arterial Pressure (Across Populations)

Categorical Variable	Moderator					
Medical Specialty	No					
Type of Intervention	No					
Category of Intervention	No					
	k	r_u	95% c.i.	p	Q_b	v
Music Medicine	3	N/A				
Music Therapy	1					
Music Preference	Yes					
Preferred	2	.44	+.28 to +.58	.00	7.42	
Non-preferred	2	.06	-.17 to +.62	.61	(p = .01)	
Level of Randomization	No					

Skin Temperature and Galvanic Skin Resistance

Mean effect sizes. Few studies examined the effects of music on skin temperature and galvanic skin resistance. The mean effect sizes were not statistically significant (Tables 35-36), and no meaningful moderator analyses could be conducted.

Table 35
Mean Effect Size for Skin Temperature

Medical Specialty	k	N	r_u	95% c.i.	p	Q
Across Specializations	4	342	.27	-.31 to .70	.33	73.2*
Cardiology/ICU	2	215	.00	-.14 to + .14	1.00	.00
Surgery	2	116	.50	-.43 to +.91	.29	12.52

p<.05, indicating that the sample is not homogeneous.

Table 36
Mean Effect Size for Galvanic Skin Resistance

Medical Specialty	k	N	r_u	95% c.i.	p	Q
Across Specializations	3	163	.15	-.04 to + .32	.13	2.53
Dentistry	2	70	.18	-.23 to + .53	.38	2.53
Surgery	1	93	.14			

Oxygen Saturation Level

Mean effect sizes. Seven studies examined the effects of music listening on subjects' oxygen saturation levels. The results are promising, even with this limited number of studies. The neonatology studies ($k = 5$) resulted in a statistically significant effect size of $r = .45$ with a homogeneous distribution of the effect sizes (Table 37). The overall mean effect size (across specializations) is significant and moderate and was also associated with a homogeneous distribution. No moderator variables were found (Table 38).

Table 37
Mean Effect Size for Oxygen Saturation Level

Medical Specialty	k	N	r_u	95% c.i.	p	Q
Across specializations	7	190	.38	+.21 to + .53	.00	8.93
Neonatology	5	145	.45	+.31 to + .59	.00	3.96
Cardiology/ICU	1	20	.26			
Pediatrics	1	25	.00			

Table 38
Moderator Analysis for Oxygen Saturation (Neonatology)

Categorical Variable	Moderator						
Category of Intervention	No						
	k	*r$_u$*	95% c.i.	*p*	*Q$_b$*	*v*	
Music Medicine	3	.40	+.22 to +.55	.00	1.86	v = .00	
Music Therapy	2	.60	+.34 to +.77	.00	(p = .17)	se(v)=.02	
Level of Randomization	No						

Secretory Immunoglobin A (sIgA)

Mean effect sizes. Four studies included the sIgA outcome measure, resulting in a medium and statistically significant effect size with a homogeneous distribution (Table 39). However, because of the limited number of studies and because of the small sample size, the Q-test may not have been able to reject homogeneity. No meaningful moderator analyses could be conducted.

Table 39
Mean Effect Size for sIgA

Medical Specialty	*k*	*N*	*r$_u$*	95% c.i.	*p*	*Q*
Across specializations	4	136	.35	+.05 to + .58	.02	5.69
Cancer/Terminal Illness/HIV	2	16	.52	-.50 to + .94	.32	3.35
Pediatrics	1	40	.41			
Dentistry	1	80	.19			

Cortisol Levels

Mean effect sizes. No statistically significant mean effect sizes were obtained for subjects' cortisol levels as a result of music or music therapy interventions. The calculation of data from six studies resulted in an effect size of $r = .00$, and data from one study only yielded a positive effect size of .34 (Table 40). No meaningful moderator analyses could be conducted.

Table 40
Mean Effect Size for Cortisol

Medical Specialty	k	N	r_u	95% c.i.	p	Q
Across Specializations	7	218	.05	-.09 to + .19	.50	2.92
Surgery	4	172	.00	-.15 to + .15	1.00	.00
Cancer/Terminal Illness/HIV	2	16	.00	-.54 to + .54	1.00	.00
General Hospital	1	30	.34			

Epinephrine And Norepinephrine Levels

Mean effect sizes. No statistically significant mean effect sizes were obtained for epinephrine or norepinephrine levels in subjects as a result of music or music therapy interventions (Tables 41-42).

Table 41
Mean Effect Size for Epinephrine

Medical Specialty	k	N	r_u	95% c.i.	p	Q
Across Specializations	3	73	.03	-.21 to + .26	.81	.31
Surgery	1	30	.00	-.23 to + .23	1.00	.00
General Hospital	1	30	.00			
Alzheimer's	1	13	.19			

Table 42
Mean Effect Size for Norepinephrine

Medical Specialty	k	N	r_u	95% c.i.	p	Q
Across specializations	3	73	.02	-.22 to + .25	.90	.08
Surgery	1	30	.00			
General Hospital	1	30	.00			
Alzheimer's	1	13	.10			

Analgesic, Sedative and Anesthetic Drug Intake

Mean effect sizes. Statistically significant results were found for the use of analgesic drug intake and sedative drug intake, but not for anesthetic drug intake. The removal of one outlier, resulted in a homogeneous distribution of effect sizes for analgesic intake in the surgery specialization, with a mean effect size of $r = .16$. For sedative intake, a mean effect size of .35 with a homogeneous distribution of the effect sizes across the surgery specialization was obtained (Tables 43-45).

Table 43
Mean Effect Size for Analgesic Drug Intake

Medical Specialty	k	N	r_u	95% c.i.	p	Q
Across Specializations	11	571	.16	+.04 to + .28	.01	17.83
Surgery	9	499	.19	+.06 to + .32	.01	15.73*
Surgery (outlier removed)[1]	8	481	.16	+.04 to +.28	.01	11.81
General Hospital	1	30	.00			
Rehabilitation	1	42	.00			

[1] Sohi (1997), r = .60
* p<.05, indicating that the sample is not homogeneous.

Table 44
Mean Effect Size for Sedative Drug Intake

Medical Specialty	k	N	r_u	95% c.i.	p	Q
Across specializations (only surgery)	6	405	.31	+.15 to + .45	.00	13.53*
Surgery (outliers removed)[1]	5	355	.35	+.20 to + .49	.00	8.77

[1] Kliempt et al. (1999), r = .01
* p<.05, indicating that the sample is not homogeneous.

Table 45
Mean Effect Size for Anesthetic Drug Intake

Medical Specialty	k	N	r_u	95% c.i.	p	Q
Across Specializations	3	220	.07	-.07 to + .19	.34	1.47
Surgery	2	136	.00	-.17 to +.17	1.00	.00
General Hospital	1	84	.17			

Moderator analysis. All studies investigating the effects of music on analgesic and/or sedative drug intake used music listening and were classified as music medicine. All but one study used client-preferred music (sedative drug intake). Therefore, no group comparisons could be conducted for these categorical variables. For analgesic drug intake, only 4 studies used client-preferred music. However, the use of client-preferred music vs. non-preferred music resulted in nearly identical findings.

Pain

Mean effect sizes. Forty-eight studies examined the effects of music on patients' pain levels, without a doubt an important outcome for medical patients. Analyses revealed that results were inconsistent across studies; however, no outliers could be identified (Table 46). Noteworthy is the large mean effect size for pain in the cancer/terminal illness/HIV specialization. Moreover, the effect sizes were consistent across studies for this medical specialization.

Table 46
Mean Effect Sizes for Pain

Medical Specialty	k	N	r_u	95% c.i.	p	Q
Across Specializations	48	2832	.21	+.15 to + .28	.00	131.76*
Surgery	22	1318	.15	+.08 to + .23	.00	33.01*
Cardiology/ICU	2	159	.35	-.29 to + .78	.27	6.78*
Cancer/Terminal Illness/HIV	4	70	.45	+.23 to + .63	.00	2.71
General Hospital	5	417	.04	-.06 to + .12	.45	.25
Neonatology	2	37	.57	+.20 to + .80	.00	1.56
OB/GYN	3	529	.14	-.12 to + .38	.30	3.05
Pediatrics	3	66	.45	-.30 to + .86	.23	17.62*
Dentistry	3	161	.18	-.17 to + .48	.31	8.58*
Rehabilitation	4	113	.42	+.02 to + .71	.04	13.89*

*p<.05, indicating that the sample is not homogeneous.

Moderator analysis. Moderator analysis revealed that music therapy interventions had a much greater effect than music medicine interventions (Table 47). Also, categories of intervention were considered an important source of the variability in effect size distribution. Medical specialty was also a significant source of variability (Q_b = .0008). Finally, level of randomization was found to be a moderator variable. One may question if the larger effect sizes associated with music therapy interventions may have been due to less rigorous study designs. A subsequent analysis, using only randomized trials, still revealed a much higher effect size for music therapy studies (k = 2, r = .74) than for music medicine studies (k = 31, r = .13). However, because of the disproportionate number of music therapy studies versus music medicine studies, great care should be taken when interpreting these results. For surgery, all studies were considered music medicine, and no moderator variables were found for this specialization.

Table 47
Moderator Analysis for Pain (Across Specializations)

Categorical Variable	Moderator						
Medical Specialty	Yes						
Type of Intervention	No						
Category of Intervention	Yes						
	k	r_u	95% c.i.	p	Q_b	v	
Music Medicine	43	.18	+.11 to +.25	.00	13.36	$v = .03$	
Music Therapy	5	.62	+.41 to +.77	.00	$(p = .00)$	se(v)=.02	
Music Preference	No						
Preferred	31	.20	+.12 to +.28	.00	.11	$v = .03$	
Non-preferred	14	.18	+.06 to +.29	.00	$(p = .74)$	se(v)=.01	
Level of Randomization	Yes						
Randomized	33	.17	+.10 to +.23	.00	20.74	$v = .02$	
Non-randomized	3	.26	-.04 to +.51	.08	$(p = .00)$	se(v) =.01	
Within-Ss	9	.58	+.42 to +.70	.00			
Unknown	3	.04	-.20 to +.27	.75			

Comfort Levels

Mean effect sizes. Two studies focused on patient comfort level. No statistically significant mean effect size was obtained (Table 48).

Table 48
Mean Effect Size for Patient Comfort Level

Medical Specialty	k	N	r_u	95% c.i.	p	Q
Across Specializations	2	61	.23	-.07 to +.46	.09	.36
General Hospital	1	52	.26			
Cancer/Terminal Illness/HIV	1	9	.00			

Nausea/Vomiting

Mean effect sizes. Four studies measured the effects of music on nausea and/or vomiting and obtained a mean effect size of $r = .20$. All studies used music listening and were considered music medicine studies (Table 49).

Table 49
Mean Effect Size for Nausea/Vomiting

Medical Specialty	k	N	r_u	95% c.i.	p	Q
Across Specializations	4	126	.20	+.02 to +.36	.03	2.87
Surgery	2	78	.09	-.14 to +.31	.43	.19
Cancer/Terminal Illness/HIV	2	48	.36	+.08 to +.60	.01	.43

Moderator analysis. All studies were classified as music medicine. Studies in cancer/terminal illness used patient-preferred music, whereas studies in surgery did not. A large difference in effect size was noted, but this difference was not significant (Table 50). No moderator variables could be identified as was to be expected by the obtained Q-value.

Food Intake

Mean effect sizes. No significant mean effect sizes were found for food intake (Table 51); this is likely due to the limited number of studies analyzed.

Weight Gain

Mean effect sizes. No statistically significant mean effect size was obtained for weight gain in neonates (Table 52).

Table 50
Moderator Analysis for Nausea/Vomiting

Categorical Variable	Moderator					
Medical Specialty	No					
Type of Intervention	No					
Category of Intervention	No					
	k	r_u	95% c.i.	p	Q_b	v
Music Medicine	4			N/A		
Music Therapy	0					
Music Preference	No					
Preferred	2	.37	+.08 to +.59	.01	2.25	v = .00
Non-preferred	2	.09	-.13 to +.31	.43	(p = .13)	se(v)=.02
Level of Randomization	No					

Table 51
Mean Effect Size for Food Intake

Medical Specialty	k	N	r_u	95% c.i.	p	Q
Across Specializations	3	138	.26	-.02 to +.45	.07	4.78
Neonatology	2	118	.16	-.03 to +.33	.10	1.04
Alzheimer's	1	20	.58			

Table 52
Mean Effect Size for Weight Gain

Medical Specialty	k	N	r_u	95% c.i.	p	Q
Neonatology	4	244	.10	-.02 to +.23	.11	2.84

Sleep and Fatigue

Mean effect sizes. Two studies included sleep, and two studies included fatigue as an outcome measure (Tables 53 and 54). Although significant small to moderate effects sizes were found for these outcome variables, because of the limited number of studies involved, these results are to be interpreted with extreme caution. No moderator analyses could be conducted because of the small k.

Table 53
Mean Effect Size for Sleep

Medical Specialty	k	N	r_u	95% c.i.	p	Q
Across populations (all surgery)	2	150	.30	+.15 to +.44	.00	.11

Table 54
Mean Effect Size for Fatigue

Medical Specialty	k	N	r_u	95% c.i.	p	Q
Across Specializations	2	120	.12	-.07 to +.31	.20	1.34
Surgery	1	58	.23			
Cancer/Terminal Illness/HIV	1	62	.03			

Motor Activity

Mean effect sizes. No statistically significant mean effect sizes were found for this outcome measure (Table 55).

Table 55
Mean Effect Size for Motor Activity

Medical Specialty	k	N	r_u	95% c.i.	p	Q
Across Specializations	6	419	.10	-.05 to + .26	.20	9.7
Neonatology	4	389	.01	-.09 to + .12	.76	1.52
Pediatrics	1	10	.35			
Fetal	1	20	.60			

In-Seat Behavior

Mean effect sizes. Two studies examined the effects of music therapy on the in-seat behavior of patients with dementia. Both studies utilized active music making. One study resulted in an effect size of .60 and the other of .70. These consistent results yielded a large mean effect size and a non-significant Q-value (Table 56).

Table 56
Mean Effect Size for In-Seat Behavior

Medical Specialty	k	N	r_u	95% c.i.	p	Q
Across Specializations (all Alzheimer's)	2	40	.62	+.37 to +.78	.00	.18

Gait

Mean effect sizes. Six studies on the effect of music therapy interventions on gait yielded a moderate effect size (Table 57). Moreover, these results were homogeneous.

Table 57
Mean Effect Size for Gait

Medical Specialty	k	N	r_u	95% c.i.	p	Q
Across Specializations (all Rehabilitation)	6	94	.38	+.17 to +.55	.00	3.74

Length of Hospital Stay

Mean effect sizes. No statistically significant mean effect size was obtained across populations for this outcome variable. However, the mean effect size for neonatology was significant and homogeneous (Table 58).

Table 58
Mean Effect Size for Length of Hospital Stay

Medical Specialty	k	N	r_u	95% c.i.	p	Q
Across Specializations	6	419	.09	-.01 to +.18	.08	.45
Neonatology	3	185	.20	+.05 to +.34	.00	.68
Surgery	3	234	.00	-.13 to +.13	1.00	.00

Anxiety (STAI)

Mean effect sizes. Many studies examined the effects of music or music therapy on anxiety, and most studies measured anxiety using the State Trait Anxiety Inventory. Results of these studies were analyzed separately from those studies that employed different measures of anxiety.

Moderate effect sizes were obtained for anxiety as measured by STAI across populations as well as for surgery, cardiology, and cancer/terminal illness. However, all of the effect sizes were associated with heterogeneity (Table 59).

Moderator analysis. When exploring the distribution of the effect sizes across populations, no outliers could be identified. A mixed effects model was fitted to the data in an attempt to identify moderator variables, and level of randomization was found to be a significant moderator variable (Table 60).

Table 59
Mean Effect Size for Anxiety (STAI)

Medical Specialty	k	N	r_u	95% c.i.	p	Q
Across Specializations[1]	40	1921	.30	+.21 to + .39	.00	161.97*
Surgery	22	1053	.31	+.16 to + .43	.00	106.92*
Cardiology/ICU	8	413	.35	+.17 to + .50	.00	25.25*
Cancer/Terminal Illness/HIV	4	165	.34	-.06 to + .64	.09	13.39*
General Hospital	4	224	.16	-.05 to + .35	.15	6.84
Rehabilitation	1	27	.38			
OB/GYN	1	39	.42			

[1] No outliers

* p<.05, indicating that the sample is not homogeneous.

Anxiety (Non-STAI)

Mean effect sizes. Nineteen studies used measurement tools other than the State-Trait Anxiety Inventory to measure patients' anxiety. After removing two outliers, an effect size of r =.20 was obtained across specializations with a homogeneous distribution of the effect sizes (Table 61).

Table 60
Moderator Analysis for Anxiety (STAI) (Across Specializations)

Categorical Variable	Moderator					
Medical Specialty	No					
Type of Intervention	No					
Category of Intervention	No					
	k	r_u	95% c.i.	p	Q_b	v
Music Medicine	38	.30	+.21 to +.38	.00	.78	$v = .06$
Music Therapy	2	.50	+.02 to +.79	.04	(p = .37)	se(v)=.02
Music Preference	No					
Preferred	23	.34	+.23 to +.45	.00	1.19	$v = .06$
Non-preferred	16	.25	+.10 to +.38	.00	(p = .28)	se(v)=.02
Level of Randomization	Yes					
Random	27	.23	+.13 to +.32	.00	9.76	$v = .05$
Non-Random	6	.51	+.32 to +.65	.00	(p = .02)	se(v)=.02
Within-Ss	4	.52	+.26 to +.71	.00		
Unknown	3	.26	-.06 to +.53	.10		

Table 61
Mean Effect Size for Anxiety (Non-STAI)

Medical Specialty	k	N	r_u	95% c.i.	p	Q
Across Specializations	19	831	.28	+.15 to + .40	.00	53.46*
Across Specializations (outliers removed)[1]	17	780	.20	+.11 to +.28	.00	20.35
Surgery	7	424	.34	+.15 to + .50	.00	20.61*
Surgery (outliers removed)[2]	5	386	.24	+.15 to +.34	.00	3.05
OB/GYN	2	42	.20	-.21 to + .55	.33	1.61
Dentistry	2	125	.00	-.18 to + .18	1.0	.00
Alzheimer's	1	20	.44			
General Hospital	1	38	.00			
Cardiology/ICU	1	23	.79			
Pediatrics	1	30	.00			

[1] Bonny (1983), r = .79; Mullooly, Levin, & Feldman (1988), r = .80
[2] Heiser, Chiles, Fudge, & Gray (1997), r =.00; Mullooly et al. (1988), r = .80
* p<.05, indicating that the sample is not homogeneous.

Moderator analysis. Exclusion of outliers resulted in a homogeneous distribution of effect sizes. Table 62 provides comparisons for categories of intervention and music preference.

Table 62
Moderator Analysis for Anxiety (Non-STAI)

Categorical Variable	Moderator					
Medical Specialty	No					
Type of Intervention	No					
Category of Intervention	No					
	k	r_u	95% c.i.	p	Q_b	v
Music Medicine	13	.16	+.08 to +.25	.00	2.37	v =.01
Music Therapy	4	.30	+.15 to +.44	.00	(p = .12)	se(v)=.01
Music Preference	No					
Preferred	9	.17	+.07 to +.27	.00	1.32	v = .00
Non-preferred	6	.25	+.15 to +.36	.00	(p = .25)	se(v)=.01
Level of Randomization	No					

Distress

Mean effect sizes. Thirteen studies examined the effect of music listening, and one study the effect of music therapy on patients' levels of distress. A homogeneous distribution of effect sizes was achieved by removing one outlier, resulting in a mean effect size of r =.24 (Table 63).

Table 63
Mean Effect Size for Distress

Medical Specialty	k	N	r_u	95% c.i.	p	Q
Across Specializations	14	631	.39	+.18 to +.56	.00	91.29*
Across specializations (outlier removed)[1]	13	607	.24	+.13 to +.35	.00	20.46
Surgery	2	86	.06	-.16 to +.27	.58	.09
Neonatology	8	287	.54	+.19 to .77	.00	75.81*
Neonatology (outliers removed)[2]	6	204	.38	+.21 to +.52	.00	6.91
Pediatrics	1	40	.45			
General Hospital	1	72	.08			
Cardiology/ICU	1	140	.19			
Cancer/Terminal Illness/HIV	1	6	.00			

[1] Brackbill, Adams, Crowell, & Gray (1966), r =. 97
[2] Brackbill et al (1966), r =.97; Owens (1979), r = .00
* p<.05, indicating that the sample is not homogeneous.

Moderator analysis. Across specializations, 5 studies used client-preferred music, and 6 did not. Effect sizes were significant for the use of preferred music, but not for non-preferred music. However, the non-preferred music group obtained a higher effect size ($r =.27$) than the preferred group ($r =.16$), but this difference was not statistically significant. Eleven studies were classified as music medicine, and two were classified as music therapy. The differences between music therapy and music medicine interventions approached significance ($p=.06$). Level of randomization was a significant moderator variable (Table 64), despite the fact that the Q-test for the mean effect size across populations resulted in a non-significant value.

Table 64
Moderator Analysis for Distress (Across Specializations)

Categorical Variable	Moderator						
Medical Specialty	No						
Type of Intervention	No						
Category of Intervention	No						
		k	r_u	95% c.i.	p	Q_b	v
Music Medicine		9	.24	+.12 to +.35	.00	.03	$v = .01$
Music Therapy		4	.22	+.03 to +.40	.00	($p = .86$)	se(v)=.01
Music Preference	No						
Preferred		5	.16	.00 to +.32	.06	1.03	$v = .01$
Non-preferred		8	.27	+.15 to +.38	.00	($p = .31$)	se(v)=.01
Level of Randomization	Yes						
Random		6	.17	+.08 to +.27	.00	9.56	$v = .00$
Non-Random		3	.20	+.04 to +.36	.01	($p =. 01$)	se(v)=.01
Within-Ss		4	.58	+.36 to +.75	.00		

Agitation

Mean effect sizes. Only studies that were within the Alzheimer's specialization examined the effects of music or music therapy on patients' agitation levels. A high mean effect size of .70 was obtained, however the results were inconsistent across studies. No outliers could be identified (Table 65).

Table 65
Mean Effect Size for Agitation

Medical Specialty	k	N	r_u	95% c.i.	p	Q
Across Specializations (all Alzheimer's)	7	170	.70	+.49 to +.83	.00	24.78*

* $p<.05$, indicating that the sample is not homogeneous.

Moderator analysis. The music medicine studies ($k = 2$) obtained a lower mean effect size than the music therapy studies, but this difference was not statistically significant. The use of preferred music versus non-preferred music did make a significant difference (Table 66).

Table 66
Moderator Analysis for Agitation (Alzheimer's)

Categorical Variable	Moderator						
Medical Specialty	N/A						
Type of Intervention	No						
Category of Intervention	No						
	k	r_u	95% c.i.	p	Q_b	v	
Music Medicine	2	.61	+.13 to +.86	.02	.43	$v = .51$	
Music Therapy	5	.73	+.51 to +.86	.00	(p = .51)	se(v)=.09	
Music Preference	Yes						
Preferred	2	.78	+.63 to +.88	.00	5.49	$v = .01$	
Non-preferred	3	.52	+.31 to +.68	.00	(p=.02)	se(v)=.03	
Level of Randomization	No						

Aggression

Mean effect sizes. Only two studies examined the effects of music on patient's levels of aggression. Both studies used music listening, were classified as music medicine, used client-preferred music, and employed a within-subjects design. The sample level effect sizes for each study were $r =.52$ and $r = .81$. Due to the small total N, the reader should exert caution when interpreting these findings (Table 67).

Table 67
Mean Effect Size for Aggression

Medical Specialty	k	N	r_u	95% c.i.	p	Q
Across Specializations (all Alzheimer's)	2	23	.57	+.16 to +.81	.01	.54

Depression

Mean effect sizes. A limited number of studies (7) investigated the effects of music or music therapy on depression levels (specifically) in medical patients, resulting in a mean effect size of $r = .26$ (Table 68). It is noted that there is some redundancy between this outcome variable and that of "Mood:" studies that included depression specifically as an outcome variable were included herein, whereas studies that measured the more global construct of mood were included in a separate outcome category.

Table 68
Mean Effect Size for Depression

Medical Specialty	k	N	r_u	95% c.i.	p	Q
Across Specializations	7	246	.26	+.13 to +.38	.00	6.28
Surgery	3	70	.41	+.18 to +.59	.00	.14
Cancer/Terminal Illness/HIV	2	100	.26	+.06 to +.93	.01	.01
Alzheimer's	1	20	.44			
Cardiology/ICU	1	15	.53			

Moderator analysis. Moderator analysis indicated that music medicine studies were less effective than music therapy studies, however, this difference was not statistically significant. Studies using preferred music yielded a higher mean effect size than those using non-preferred music, but this difference was also not statistically significant (Table 69).

Table 69
Moderator Analysis for Depression (Across Specializations)

Categorical Variable	Moderator					
Medical Specialty	No					
Type of Intervention	No					
Category of Intervention	No					
	k	r_u	95% c.i.	p	Q_b	v
Music Medicine	4	.21	+.04 to +.38	.02	.61	v = .00
Music Therapy	3	.31	+.13 to +.47	.00	(p = .43)	se(v)=.01
Music Preference	No					
Preferred	3	.32	+.13 to +.48	.00	1.69	v = .00
Non-preferred	2	.13	-.09 to +.34	.26	(p = .19)	se(v)=.02
Level of Randomization	No					

Mood

Mean effect sizes. A substantial mean effect size of .44 was found for the global outcome measure of mood across specializations (Table 70), although these results are not homogenous.

Table 70
Mean Effect Size for Mood

Medical Specialty	k	N	r_u	95% c.i.	p	Q
Across Specializations	11	358	.44	+.23 to + .60	.00	38.87*
Cancer/Terminal Illness/HIV	4	170	.26	+.12 to + .40	.00	2.77
Pediatrics	2	42	.64	+.40 to + .79	.00	.22
Alzheimer's	2	48	.76	+.36 to + .93	.00	2.07
Surgery	1	64	.27			
Rehabilitation	1	14	.66			
Cardiology/ICU	1	20	.07			

*p<.05, indicating that the sample is not homogeneous.

Moderator analysis. Table 71 lists moderator analyses results for mood. Music preference was found to be a moderator variable. Whereas effect sizes for music therapy treatment were higher than for than music medicine interventions, this difference was not statistically significant.

Table 71
Moderator Analysis for Mood (Across Specializations)

Categorical Variable	Moderator					
Medical Specialty	No					
Type of Intervention	No					
Category of Intervention	No					
	k	r_u	95% c.i.	p	Q_b	v
Music Medicine	3	.17	-.21 to +.51	.38	2.98	v = .07
Music Therapy	8	.52	+.32 to +.67	.00	(p = .08)	se(v)=.05
Music Preference	Yes					
Preferred	2	.78	+.63 to +.88	.00	5.49	v = .01
Non-preferred	3	.52	+.31 to +.68	.00	(p = .02)	se(v)=.03
Level of Randomization	No					

Feelings of Control

Mean effect sizes. Only two studies measured patients' levels of control (Table 72), and a homogeneous effect size (approaching large) was achieved; however, because of the limited number of studies, these results should be interpreted with extreme caution.

Table 72
Mean Effect Size for Feelings of Control

Medical Specialty	*k*	*N*	r_u	*95% c.i.*	*p*	*Q*
Across Specializations	2	68	.46	+.25 to +.64	.00	.88
Pediatrics	1	32	.48			
Dentistry	1	36	.45			

Well-Being and Life Satisfaction

Mean effect sizes. Six studies examined well-being and life satisfaction as outcome variables. A mean effect size across populations of *r* = .27 was obtained (Table 73).

Moderator analysis. Two studies were classified as music medicine, and 4 as music therapy. Music therapy was more effective than music medicine for this outcome, but this difference was not statistically significant (Table 74).

Table 73
Mean Effect Size for Well-Being/ Life Satisfaction

Medical Specialty	*k*	*N*	r_u	*95% c.i.*	*p*	*Q*
Across Specializations	6	248	.27	+.12 to +.41	.00	6.22
Cancer/Terminal Illness/HIV	4	147	.24	+.06 to +.40	.01	2.58
Alzheimer's	1	43	.50			
Surgery	1	58	.18			

Table 74
Moderator Analysis for Well-Being and Life Satisfaction (Across Specializations)

Categorical Variable	Moderator					
Medical Specialty	No					
Type of Intervention	No					
Category of Intervention	No					
	k	r_u	95% c.i.	*p*	Q_b	*v*
Music Medicine	2	.16	-.09 to +.39	.20	1.27	v = .00
Music Therapy	4	.32	+.17 to +.46	.00	(p = .26)	se(v)=.01
Music Preference	No					
Preferred	1		N/A			
Non-preferred	2					
Level of Randomization	No					

Social Interaction

Mean effect sizes. All studies examining this outcome variable were categorized as music therapy and within the medical specialization of Alzheimer's. Effect sizes were distributed widely, however no moderator variables could be identified (Table 75).

Table 75
Mean Effect Size for Social Interaction

Medical Specialty	k	N	r_u	95% c.i.	p	Q
Alzheimer's	5	123	.63	+.16 to +.87	.01	31.05*

*p<.05, indicating that the sample is not homogeneous.

Speech/Verbalization

Mean effect sizes. Seven studies examined the effect of music therapy on patients' speech/verbalization with a very large effect size of .61 (Table 76). Moreover, the distribution of effect sizes was homogeneous.

Table 76
Mean Effect Size for Speech/Verbalization

Medical Specialty	k	N	r_u	95% c.i.	p	Q
Across Specializations	7	127	.61	+.38 to +.76	.00	12.9
Alzheimer's	4	43	.75	+.48 to +.89	.00	4.83
Rehabilitation	2	44	.30	-.10 to +.63	.14	1.45
Pediatrics	1	40	.65			

Attention

Mean effect sizes. No statistically significant mean effect size was obtained for the outcome variable of attention. The small total sample size and the limited number of studies likely contributed to the lack of significant results (Table 77)

Table 77
Mean Effect Size for Attention

Medical Specialty	k	N	r_u	95% c.i.	p	Q
Alzheimer's	2	22	.29	-.19 to +.66	.24	.08

Cognitive Functioning

Mean effect sizes. The effect sizes of these studies varied widely yielding heterogeneous, non-significant findings (Table 78). No outliers could be identified.

Table 78
Mean Effect Size for Cognitive Functioning

Medical Specialty	k	N	r_u	95% c.i.	p	Q
Alzheimer's	6	139	.28	-.11 to +.59	.15	23.47*

*p<.05, indicating that the sample is not homogeneous.

Moderator analysis. For this outcome variable, music medicine interventions yielded a mean effect size that was not statistically significant. However, the music therapy interventions yielded a mean effect size that approached statistical significance (Table 79). These two interventions did not differ significantly from each other.

Table 79
Moderator Analysis for Cognitive Functioning

Categorical Variable	Moderator						
Medical Specialty	N/A						
Type of Intervention	No						
Category of Intervention	No						
	k	r_u	95% c.i.	p	Q_b	v	
Music Medicine	3	.13	-.31 to +.52	.58	.91	$v = .11$	
Music Therapy	3	.42	-.02 to +.72	.06	(p = .34)	se(v)=.09	
Music Preference	No						
Preferred	0	N/A					
Non-preferred	3						
Level of Randomization	No						

SUMMARY

Table 80 provides a list of all mean symptom level effect sizes (across specializations) in descending order of effect size magnitude.

Table 80
Mean Symptom Level Effect Sizes (Across Specializations)
in Descending Order [1]

Symptom	k	N	r_u	95% c.i.	p	Q
Agitation	7	170	.70	+.49 to +.83	.00	24.78*
Social Interaction	5	123	.63	+.16 to +.87	.01	31.05*
In-Seat Behavior	2	40	.62	+.37 to + .78	.00	.18
Speech/Verbalization	7	127	.61	+.38 to +.76	.00	12.9
Aggression	2	23	.57	+.16 to +.81	.01	.54
Feelings of Control	2	68	.46	+.25 to +.64	.00	.88
Mood	11	358	.44	+.23 to + .60	.00	38.87*
Gait	6	94	.38	+.17 to +.55	.00	3.74
Oxygen Saturation Level	7	190	.38	+.21 to + .53	.00	8.93
Sedative Drug Intake	5	355	.35	+.20 to +.49	.00	8.77
Secretory IgA	4	136	.35	+.05 to + .58	.02	5.69
Mean Arterial Pressure	4	192	.31	+.06 to +.52	.02	8.54*
Anxiety (STAI)	40	1921	.30	+.21 to + .39	.00	161.97*
Sleep	2	150	.30	+.15 to +.44	.00	.11
Attention	2	22	.29	-.19 to + .66	.24	.08
Cognitive Functioning	6	139	.28	-.11 to +.59	.15	23.47*
Skin Temperature	4	342	.27	-.31 to +.70	.33	73.2*
Well-being /Life Satisfaction	6	248	.27	+.12 to +.41	.00	6.22
Depression	7	246	.26	+.13 to+.38	.00	6.28
Respiration Rate	21	731	.26	+.15 to +.36	.00	38.11*
Food Intake	3	138	.26	-.02 to + .45	.07	4.78
Distress	13	607	.24	+.13 to +.35	.00	20.46
Heart Rate	42	1805	.24	+.15 to +.32	.00	138.93*
Pain	49	2872	.23	+.15 to + .23	.00	137.09*
Comfort Level	2	61	.23	-.07 to +.46	.09	.36
Anxiety (non-STAI)	17	780	.20	+.11 to +.28	.00	20.35
Nausea/Vomiting	4	126	.20	+.02 to + .36	.03	2.87
Systolic Blood Pressure	21	1055	.19	+.11 to +.26	.00	27.62
Diastolic Blood Pressure	18	1029	.18	+.09 to +.27	.00	34.96*
Blood Pressure	7	332	.17	-.01 to + .35	.07	13.74*
Analgesic Drug Intake	11	571	.16	+.04 to + .28	.01	17.83
Galvanic Skin Resistance	3	163	.15	-.04 to + .32	.13	2.53
Fatigue	2	120	.12	-.07 to +.31	.20	1.34
Motor Activity	6	419	.10	-.05 to +.26	.20	9.7
Weight	4	244	.10	-.02 to +.23	.11	2.84
Length of Hospital Stay	6	419	.09	-.01 to +.18	.08	.45
Anesthetic Drug Intake	3	220	.07	-.07 to + .19	.34	1.47
Cortisol	7	218	.05	-.09 to + .19	.50	2.92
Ephinephrine	3	73	.03	-.21 to + .26	.81	.31
Norepinephrine	3	73	.02	-.22 to + .25	.90	.08

[1] All outliers removed   *p<.05, indicating that the sample is not homogeneous.

4

DISCUSSION

In this chapter, selected meta-analytic results are discussed with implications for future research and evidence-based music medicine and music therapy practice. It is important to emphasize at the beginning that the authors are deliberately assuming a conservative and cautious position with the interpretation of these data, in spite of their personal enthusiasm and optimism for the potential implications of these findings.

Sample-Level Results

Mean Effect Sizes for Medical Specializations

The 183 studies included in this review examined the effects of a variety of treatment approaches (music listening, music-based relaxation, music and imagery, active music making and combined approaches) on a wide range of dependent variables. This analysis revealed a mean effect size of $r = .29$, and this was considered a moderate, significant effect size. However, this encouraging finding needs to be interpreted very cautiously. Because of the wide variety of study characteristics, combining the sample-level effect sizes for all 183 studies has the potential to lack meaning, both clinically and statistically. The results of these studies overall were not homogeneous (as indicated by the Q-value), and more meaningful results were found when the studies were categorized according to medical specialty or outcome measure.

The largest mean sample-level effect sizes were obtained for Alzheimer's and fetal studies. The Alzheimer's specialization contained the highest number of music therapy vs. music medicine studies (21 versus 5) of all the specializations. It is indeed tempting to conclude that the use of music therapy interventions likely contributed to the large mean sample-level effect size for this specialty. However, it is important to point out that many of the Alzheimer's studies used a within-subject design rather than a more rigorous randomized design. Of the 183 studies included in this review, 29% used within-subject designs. In contrast, 73 % of the Alzheimer's studies used a within-subject design. Consistently throughout this meta-analytic review, within-subject designs contributed to higher effect sizes. Therefore, it is possible that the high mean effect size found in the Alzheimer's studies might have been influenced by the design of the studies.

Studies examining the effects of music on fetal responses led to an equally high mean effect size. However, only four studies were included in this review, and three used a within-subjects design (potentially inflating the effect sizes). This small number of studies resulted in a much larger confidence interval in this specialization when compared to the other specializations. Even so, these effect sizes were homogeneously distributed. This suggests that music may be an effective intervention within this specialization, but additional research is needed.

Results of the meta-analysis of studies in pediatrics and rehabilitation also revealed substantial mean sample-level effect sizes. In the pediatric specialty, the mean effect size was associated with excess variability, however, the category of intervention appeared to be an important source of this variability: music therapy interventions ($k = 5$, $r = .49$) were found significantly more effective than music medicine interventions ($k = 5$, $r = .13$). Moreover, the experimental conditions in the music medicine studies did not lead to significantly better results than the control conditions. All music therapy studies used active music therapy interventions. These results may provide evidence that, in pediatric medical settings, playing music *with* the child is more effective than playing music *for* the child.

Most studies in the rehabilitation group examined the effects of music therapy on gait parameters or speech. Music medicine studies with this population focused on pain and anxiety management. The homogeneous set of effect sizes leading to a mean effect size of $r = .38$ with a small confidence interval strongly suggests that music medicine or music therapy are effective interventions in rehabilitation.

Meta-analytic results for the specializations of cardiology/ICU, neonatology, surgery, OB/GYN, and cancer/terminal illness/AIDS revealed mean effect sizes between $r =. 21$ and $r = .24$. According to Cohen's guidelines, these approach values that are considered moderate. Many studies in cardiology/ICU, surgery, OB/GYN and neonatology were classified as music medicine studies that used music listening as the experimental condition. Only the cancer/terminal illness/AIDS group had a more equal distribution of music medicine versus music therapy studies. Because music therapy studies in other medical specializations led consistently to higher effect sizes than music medicine studies, it is possible that lower mean effect sizes in cardiology/ICU, surgery, OB/GYN and neonatology could be a function of the category of intervention (music medicine versus music therapy). More music therapy studies are urgently needed within these medical specializations so that the effects of music therapy interventions can be adequately assessed.

Meta-analyses of studies in the general hospital and dental specializations yielded the smallest effect sizes. Despite a relatively large sample size ($N = 703$), the mean effect size for the general hospital studies was significant but small ($r = .12$). Within this specialization, all studies were classified as music medicine and used music listening as the intervention during a variety of painful or uncomfortable procedures and medical tests (e.g., bronchoscopy, femoral angiography, laceration repair, sigmoidoscopy). It's possible that the small mean effect size can be attributed to the diversity of these procedures and the severity and range of subjects' clinical conditions. It is also possible that other interventions (i.e., those that actively engage the patient musically in pain and anxiety management) would demonstrate higher levels of effectiveness. Similarly, all dental studies used music listening, and this intervention yielded a small effect size of $r = .16$. This effect size was statistically non-significant, meaning that the experimental condition did not lead to results that differed significantly from the control condition. As many of the dental studies led to an effect size of $r = .00$, the current use of music listening as a treatment intervention during dental procedures should be re-examined, and other types of music interventions should be tested in future studies.

Active Engagement of the Patient

Music therapy studies comprised only 29% of the total number of studies included in this review. Nearly all music therapy studies actively engaged the patient in the session (instrumental play or singing). A comparison of the effectiveness of studies using music therapy versus music medicine indicated that, overall, music therapy interventions ($r = .40$) were significantly more effective than music medicine interventions ($r = .24$). Of course, it is possible that these results may have been influenced by other variables. One possible confounding variable is the level of randomization used in a number of music therapy studies (i.e., within-subjects designs), as these are known to contribute to higher effect sizes than randomized trials. A subsequent analysis, however, using randomized trials alone, suggested that music therapy interventions ($k = 18, r = .43$) were, in fact, more effective than music medicine interventions ($k = 74, r = .22$).

These results imply that although music listening (pre-recorded music) may have therapeutic benefits for medical patients, music therapy interventions, involving a trained music therapist, a relationship and a therapeutic process can produce significantly greater effects in clinical outcomes.

Music Preference

For studies that examined the effects of music listening, the use of patient-selected music (preferred music) ($k = 75, r = .28$) led to very similar results as the use of researcher-selected music (i.e., not taking patients' preferences into account) ($k = 73, r = .24$). Even after exclusion of the neonatology and fetal specializations (as no music preference could be expressed by the subjects in these groups), very similar results were obtained. This finding was rather surprising in light of the emphasis in the music therapy literature on the importance of using patient-preferred music. In an attempt to find an explanation for this, studies using patient-preferred music were reviewed. It was found that, in most cases, patients were presented with a limited number of music selections from which they were asked to select music that appealed to them. It could well be that patients selected a style of music from the available options that they liked best (or disliked least), but this may not have been their preferred music. It appears that definitions of 'preferred music' varied widely across studies, and this may be a significant factor influencing the current results.

It is important to point out that in the surgery specialization, the use of patient-selected music did actually lead to a higher mean effect size ($r = .34$ vs. $r = .15$) than experimenter-selected music, and this difference approached statistical significance ($p = .07$). Moreover, those studies that did not take patient preference into account resulted in a mean effect size that was not statistically significant. In cardiology/ICU, the use of patient-selected music produced better results ($r = .36$ vs. $r = .21$), but this difference was not statistically significant. Similarly, in Alzheimer's studies, slightly higher effect sizes were obtained for studies that used patient-preferred music ($r = .64$ vs. $r = .53$), but this difference was again not statistically significant.

Level of Randomization

Fifty percent of the studies (excluding outliers) included in this review used randomized trials. The use of less rigorous designs comprised 41 % of the total number of studies: 13% used non-randomized trials and 28% used within-subject designs. For nine percent of the studies, randomization procedures were not adequately reported. Less rigorous designs resulted in higher effect sizes than randomized trials. The difference in effects sizes between randomized studies ($r = .24$) and within-subject designs ($r = .47$) was statistically significant. This indicates that the use of within-subject designs may have inflated the actual effect of the treatment. Therefore, results from studies using within-subject designs should be interpreted conservatively. A comparable number of within-subject designs were used in the music medicine studies ($k = 24$) as in the music therapy studies ($k = 27$). However, in calculating percentages of within-subjects designs used among all the studies included in this review, it was found 18.9 % of music medicine studies versus 50.9% of music therapy studies used within-subjects designs. An analysis of music therapy studies using these designs led to a higher mean effect size than the music medicine studies using these designs ($r = .51$ vs. $r = .44$), but this difference was not statistically significant. As stated previously, to examine this potential bias, randomized music therapy studies were compared to randomized music medicine studies. Music therapy randomized trials led to a significantly higher mean effect size ($r = .43$) than randomized music medicine studies ($r = .22$). These data suggest that, with comparable levels of randomization, music therapy interventions are more effective than those used in music medicine studies.

Clinical Relevance

Therapists, administrators, and policy makers are often quite interested in the practical implications of statistical findings and may seek to understand the relevance of the small, moderate and large effect sizes of a meta-analytic review for music therapy clinical work. Rosenthal and Rubin (1983) have developed a way to illustrate the magnitude and relative importance of an effect size by displaying the percentage of improvement of the treatment versus the control group. This computation is known as the *Binomial Effect Size Display* (BESD) and is used frequently by meta-analysts. For most readers, it is easier to understand the magnitude of an effect if it is expressed as the difference between percentages of success rates (i.e., treatment vs. control) than if it is expressed as a correlational effect size (Lipsey & Wilson, 2001).

The BESD assumes that the success threshold, by definition, is always at 50% for the combined distributions. To calculate the success rate of an intervention, half of the effect size is added (for treatment group) or subtracted (control group) to the success threshold (50%) if the effect size is positive and confirms the hypothesis. For example, an effect size of $r = .40$ is translated into a success rate of 50% + 40/2 for the treatment group and 50% - 40/2 for the control group, resulting in a success rate of 70% versus 30%. Using the BESD, the following success rates were calculated for the mean sample-level effect sizes (Table 81):

Table 81
BESD Across Specializations

Medical Specialty	Experimental Success Rate	Control Success Rate
Across Specializations	64.5%	35.5%
Surgery	61%	39%
Cardiology/ICU	60.5%	39.5%
Cancer/Terminal Illness/AIDS	61%	39%
Fetal	78.5%	21.5%
General Hospital	56%	44%
Neonatology	60.5%	39.5%
OB/GYN	61.5%	38.5%
Pediatrics	67%	33%
Dental	58%	42%
Alzheimer's	78.5%	21.5%
Rehabilitation	69%	31%

These data should be interpreted with caution, however. Although this display allows for an easy and quick interpretation of the effect sizes in this review, still warranted is a careful examination of the distribution of the effect sizes and the confidence interval associated with the mean effect size as presented in Chapter 3.

Symptom-Level Results

In this section, study conclusions regarding specific outcome measures are highlighted in text boxes, with more detailed discussion following.

> ### Heart Rate
> **Music listening may be an effective intervention for heart rate reduction in surgical, cardiology/intensive care patients when patient-selected music is used. Music listening may also be beneficial for heart rate normalization in neonates.**

Moderate effect sizes were obtained for heart rate ($k = 42$, $r = .24$). Almost all studies demonstrating this effect were classified as music medicine and involved surgical patients ($k = 16$) or cardiology/intensive care patients ($k = 12$). With the exception of neonatology ($k = 5$), there were too few studies in the other specializations to allow for meaningful interpretations. An initial analysis revealed that heart rate changes in response to music in surgical patients were inconsistent across studies. However, further analyses revealed that music preference acted as a moderator variable: patients who listened to self-selected (preferred) had much lower heart rates ($r = .32$) than patients who listened to researcher-selected music ($r = .02$), and this difference was statistically significant. Cardiology/ICU patients reacted in a similar fashion: self-selected (preferred) music was more beneficial for decreasing heart rate ($r = .21$) than researcher-selected music ($r = .05$). Even though this difference did not reach statistical significance for the cardiology/ICU specialization, the results suggest that clinicians should take patient preference into account when using music listening with these types of patients. Neonates' heart rates were also influenced positively by music ($r = .30$), and this result was consistent across studies ($k = 5$). However, more studies are needed in this specialization to illustrate this effect i.e., to reduce the confidence interval associated with the mean effect size.

> ### Respiration Rate
> **Music listening may positively affect respiration rate in cardiology/ICU patients and surgical patients, however, more studies are needed.**

Small to moderate mean effect sizes were obtained for respiration rate outcomes in surgical patients ($k = 6$, $r = .19$) and cardiology/ICU patients ($k = 5$, $r = .37$). These effect sizes were consistent across studies after exclusion of extreme values. There were insufficient numbers of studies with respiration rate as an outcome variable in other medical specializations to perform meta-analysis procedures. Across specializations, a moderate effect size of $r = .26$ was obtained; however this effect size was associated with excess variability. Additional studies, especially those involving music therapy interventions, are needed to examine music's effects on respiratory rate.

Blood Pressure and Mean Arterial Pressure
Surgical patients may show moderate blood pressure and arterial pressure changes in response to music listening. Patient-selected music may lead to significantly better results.

Small but significant effect sizes were obtained for systolic blood pressure ($k = 21$, $r = .19$) and diastolic blood pressure ($k = 18$, $r = .18$) across specializations after exclusion of extreme values. Studies that reported non-specific blood pressure findings resulted in an equally small mean effect size ($k = 7$, $r = .17$). Only the systolic blood pressure outcomes were consistent across studies and across specializations. However, larger effect sizes were obtained for systolic ($r = .26$) as well as diastolic blood pressure ($r = .23$) outcomes in surgical patients. The diastolic blood pressure response was strongly mediated by music preference: patient-selected music led to a significantly higher effect size ($r = .33$) when compared with researcher-selected music ($r = .00$). Systolic blood pressure outcomes showed a similar trend ($r = .21$ vs. $r = .15$), but this difference was not statistically significant.

Outcomes for mean arterial pressure ($k = 4$) yielded a moderate effect size of $r = .31$, but results were mediated by music preference: patient-preferred music resulted in a higher mean effect size ($k = 2$, $r = .44$) than researcher-selected music ($k = 2$, $r = .06$).

Skin Temperature, Galvanic Skin Resistance and Double Pulse Index
No meaningful conclusions could be drawn for skin temperature, galvanic skin resistance, and double pulse index because of the limited number of studies.

The mean effect sizes for skin temperature ($r = .27$) and galvanic skin response ($r = .15$) were not statistically significant. More studies are needed to increase statistical power and to make meaningful interpretations. A large mean effect size ($r = .79$) for double pulse index was found. However, this effect size was based on two studies only.

Oxygen Saturation Level
Music listening appears to be highly effective in increasing oxygen saturation levels, especially in neonates.

Of all the physiological outcome variables in this review, the highest mean effect size ($r = .38$, across specializations) was found for oxygen saturation levels. The mean effect size for this outcome in the neonatology specialization was even higher ($r = .45$), and results were consistent across studies. Because of the relatively small confidence interval associated with this mean effect size, the current data strongly suggest that neonates who listen to music increase their oxygen saturation level by 72.5% compared to a 27.5% increase by the control group. More studies on oxygen saturation responses to music are needed in other specializations.

Secretory Immunoglobin A
Music listening or music therapy may significantly increase sIgA, but more studies are needed to validate these preliminary findings.

Promising results were obtained for sIgA outcomes. An analysis of studies (two music medicine and two music therapy) resulted in a moderate mean effect size of $r = .35$. This means that both music listening and music therapy interventions respectively improved patients' immune system functioning by 67.5%, compared to a 32.5% increase in the control group. These results were consistent across studies, although additional studies are needed to validate these findings.

Cortisol Levels
Larger sample sizes and more detailed statistical reporting are needed before conclusions can be drawn concerning cortisol outcomes.

Five music medicine studies and two music therapy studies included cortisol as an outcome measure. Results from six of the seven studies led to an effect size computation of $r = .00$. Unfortunately, in most studies not enough statistical detail was available to make accurate statistical computations. Also, because of the small sample sizes in these studies, there was insufficient statistical power to obtain a significant p-level. However, this does not necessarily imply that these interventions were ineffective in increasing cortisol levels, but that these effects were unable to be determined. Across populations, a very small mean effect size of $r = .05$ was obtained. Additional studies with larger samples and more detailed statistical reporting would allow more meaningful conclusions to be drawn.

Epinephrine and Norepinephrine
Preliminary studies do not support the effects of music on epinephrine and norepinephrine levels.

Very low and non-significant mean effect sizes were obtained for epinephrine and norepinephrine outcomes. However, because of the limited number of studies and the small sample sizes of these studies, it was impossible to obtain sufficient statistical power. Most studies involved music medicine interventions. Additional research, especially involving the use of music therapy interventions, is needed.

Analgesic Drug Intake
Music listening may slightly reduce the need for analgesic drugs in surgical patients.

Eight studies examining the effects of music listening on the need for and intake of analgesic drugs in surgery patients resulted in a small mean effect size of $r = .16$. Although seemingly small, this reduction of analgesics was consistent across studies, and this can be considered an important finding. Studies are needed to examine the effects of music therapy interventions on analgesic demand in patients.

Sedative Drug Intake
Music listening may be effective in reducing the need for sedatives in surgical patients.

In comparison to analgesic drug intake, larger effect sizes were obtained for the effects of music listening on sedative drug intake in surgical patients ($k= 5$; $r = .35$). Again, results were consistent across studies.

Anesthetic Drug Intake
Preliminary studies show little to no effect on anesthetic drug intake; however, additional studies are needed.

Only three studies examined the effects of music listening on patients' anesthetic drug intake. Two studies with surgical patients led to a mean effect size of $r = .00$. One general hospital study reported an effect size of $r = .17$. Additional research is needed before meaningful conclusions can be drawn.

Pain
Inconsistent study findings concerning the effects of music medicine or music therapy on patients' pain levels make interpretation difficult. Additional music therapy studies are urgently needed.

Results concerning the effects of music listening or music therapy on pain reduction were inconsistent across specializations, with a mean effect size of $r = .21$ ($k = 48$). The medical specialization involved, as well as the type of intervention and level of randomization, contributed to the heterogeneous distribution of the effect sizes across specializations. Music therapy interventions appeared to be much more effective than music medicine interventions for pain management. Even after excluding the less rigorous within-subjects designs, analyses revealed that music therapy studies yielded higher effect sizes than music medicine studies. However, the disproportionate number of music therapy versus music medicine studies warrants a cautious interpretation of these results. Clearly, more music therapy studies are needed to confirm these findings.

Twenty-two studies examined the effects of music listening on surgical patient's pain perception and resulted in a small effect size of $r = .15$. Large and more consistent results were obtained for pain reduction in cancer/terminal illness/AIDS patients ($r = .45$). Even though 3 out of 4 studies used a within-subject design, this level of randomization was not an influencing factor ($Q_b = 43$, $p = .51$). Interventions for rehabilitation and pediatric patients led also to higher effect sizes, $r = .42$ and $r = .45$, respectively, but results were inconsistent across studies. Nearly all studies ($k = 43$) were music medicine studies, and only 5 music therapy studies qualified for inclusion in this review. However, significantly higher effect sizes were found for music therapy interventions in spite of the small number of studies. More music therapy studies are urgently needed to examine whether music therapy interventions can lead to better and more consistent pain reduction in medical patients.

> ### Comfort Levels
> **No meaningful conclusions could be drawn for effects on patients' comfort levels because of the limited number of studies**

Only two studies examined the effects of music on patients' comfort levels, and there were inconsistent findings: one study (general hospital) reported an effect of $r = .26$, and one study (cancer) reported non-significant findings which translated into an effect size of $r = .00$. The latter may represent an underestimation of the true effect; nevertheless, more studies are needed before meaningful conclusions may be drawn.

> ### Nausea/Vomiting
> **Music listening may help to reduce nausea/vomiting in surgical and cancer patients.**

When analyzed across specializations, small to moderate effects sizes were found for the influence of music listening on nausea/vomiting in surgical and cancer patients. These results were consistent across studies. A larger effect size was found for the use of patient-preferred music listening vs. experimenter-selected music, although this was not significant.

> ### Food Intake
> **No significant effects sizes were found for food intake in the limited number of available studies.**

Only three studies examined the effects of music on food intake in premature infants or Alzheimer's patients. No significant effect sizes were found for this outcome variable.

> ### Weight Gain
> **No significant effect size for weight gain in neonates was found in the limited number of available studies.**

Four studies examined the effects of music listening on weight gain in premature infants, and no significant effect size was found.

Sleep and Fatigue
**No meaningful conclusions could be drawn for sleep and fatigue
outcomes because of the limited number of studies.**

Only two studies investigated the effects of music to increase sleep or reduce fatigue respectively. Although small to moderate effect sizes were found for these outcome variables, these results should be interpreted with extreme caution.

Motor Activity
**Music listening does not appear to influence motor activity
based on limited, preliminary findings.**

Several studies ($k = 4$) examined the effects of music listening on motor activity in fetuses, premature infants and pediatrics. Although additional studies are needed, preliminary findings indicate that there is no significant effect.

In-Seat Behavior
**Preliminary results suggest that music therapy may be effective
in improving in-seat behavior in Alzheimer's patients.**

Two studies examined the effects of music therapy (active music-making) on the in-seat behavior of Alzheimer's patients, and a very large and consistent effect size was found ($k = 2$, $r = .62$). However, because this effect is based on the results of such a limited number of studies, it should be interpreted with a great deal of caution. Additional studies are needed to validate these results.

Gait
**Music therapy appears to be effective in normalizing gait parameters of
rehabilitation patients with motor disturbances.**

Noteworthy are the results for gait ($k = 6$, $r = .38$), as 69% improvements were found in the experimental groups compared to 31% in the control groups. All studies used music therapy, i.e., rhythmic auditory cueing or stimulation, to improve gait in patients suffering from stroke, traumatic brain injury and gross motor dysfunction. Even though most studies used small sample sizes, combining their effect sizes led to strong and homogeneous statistical findings.

Hospital Stay
**Music listening may reduce the length of
hospital stay for premature infants.**

Three studies provided consistent findings regarding the effects of music listening in decreasing the length of hospital stay for premature infants ($r = .20$).

Although more studies are needed to strengthen this finding, this effect is noteworthy.

In contrast, no significant effects ($r = .00$) for reduced length of hospital stay were found for surgical patients. Unfortunately, these studies ($k = 3$) did not report detailed statistical information so it is possible that this mean effect size is an underestimation of the true effect.

Anxiety
Music listening may decrease anxiety in surgical and cardiology/ICU patients. More studies are needed in other medical specializations.

Moderate mean effect sizes were found for state anxiety reduction, as measured by the State-Trait Anxiety Inventory, in surgical ($r = .31$) and in cardiology/ICU patients ($r = .35$), however, theses results were inconsistent across studies. This inconsistency was attributable to varying levels of randomization: the use of more rigorously controlled designs yielded significantly lower effect sizes than less rigorous designs. Study results for anxiety in cancer/terminal illness/AIDS patients as well as in general hospital patients varied greatly, leading to statistically insignificant results.

More consistent results were obtained in studies measuring anxiety with tools other than STAI (e.g., the Visual Analog Scale). A homogeneous mean effect size of $r = .20$ was found across specializations. A slightly higher mean effect size of $r = .24$ was obtained for surgical patients. However, there was a maximum of two studies that examined this outcome in each of the other specializations, and no meaningful conclusions could be drawn for those patient groups.

Overall, music therapy studies were greatly underrepresented in this analysis (7 music therapy vs. 52 music medicine studies), and additional music therapy studies are warranted.

Distress
Music listening may reduce distress behaviors, including crying, in premature infants.

Most studies examining the influence of music on levels of distress were conducted with premature infants ($k = 6$ with outliers removed), and results yielded a consistent mean effect size of $r = .38$. It is important to point out that within-subject study designs in this specialization resulted in a much higher mean effect size ($k = 3$, $r = .79$) than randomized ($k = 2$, $r = .28$) and non-randomized ($k = 2$, $r = .11$) control group designs, and level of randomization was found to be a moderator variable. A maximum of two studies were conducted within each of the other specializations; therefore no meaningful interpretations could be made.

**Music therapy may be effective in reducing
agitation in Alzheimer's patients.**

A number of studies examined agitation outcomes in Alzheimer's patients (k =7), and analyses revealed a very large mean effect size of r = .70. It is important to note that music preference played a significant role in reducing agitation in elderly patients: patient-preferred music led to significantly better results than researcher-selected music (r = .78 vs. r = .52).

Most of these studies involved specially designed music therapy interventions to actively engage patients, and these approaches are likely to have contributed to the large effects size obtained. However, it is also important to point out that many of these studies used a within-subject design, possibly inflating the effect sizes. Therefore, the reader should interpret these results with some caution.

Aggression
**Preliminary results suggest that music therapy may be effective
in reducing aggression in Alzheimer's patients.**

Two studies examined the effects of patient-preferred music listening on aggression in Alzheimer's patients. A large and consistent effect size was found (r= .57), however, it is important to interpret these results with caution because of the small number of studies and the use of a within-subjects design in both.

Depression and Mood
**Music therapy or music medicine may be effective in decreasing
depression and enhancing mood in medical patients.**

Music therapy interventions were found to have larger effect sizes than music medicine interventions in improving mood (r = .52 vs. r = .17) and in decreasing depression (r = .31 vs. r = .21) in medical patients, although not significantly so. In addition, patient-preferred music resulted in greater treatment effectiveness than researcher-selected music in enhancing the more general outcome of mood. Depression reduction through music was consistent across populations (r = .26). Mood enhancement was significantly better in pediatric (k = 2, r = .64) and Alzheimer's patients (k = 2, r = 75) than in cancer/terminal illness/AIDS patients (k = 4, r = .26). However, because of the limited number of studies analyzed, these findings should be interpreted with caution.

> ### *Feelings of Control*
> **No meaningful conclusions could be drawn for the effects**
> **of music on patients' feelings of control**
> **because of the limited number of studies available.**

Two studies examined the effects of music on patients' perceived levels of control, leading to a mean effect size of $r = .46$. The fact that the two studies arrived at similar effect sizes is encouraging, however, additional studies examining this outcome measure are needed.

> ### *Well-Being and Life Satisfaction*
> **Music therapy interventions may improve**
> **patient well-being and life satisfaction.**

Studies that examined the effects of music on medical patients' reports of well-being and life satisfaction were combined because of the limited number of studies, and results indicated a mean effect size of $r = .27$. Interestingly, music therapy studies led to statistically significant and consistent findings ($r = .32$), whereas music medicine interventions did not ($r = .16$).

> ### *Social Interaction*
> **Music therapy may be effective in improving**
> **social interaction in Alzheimer's patients.**

An analysis of the effects of music therapy on social interaction among Alzheimer's patients ($k = 5$), revealed large mean effect sizes of $r = .63$. However, these effects were inconsistent across studies, ranging from $r = .17$ to $r = .89$, and no moderator variables could be identified. This large mean effect size is not surprising given that music therapy interventions are geared to actively engaging patients in music experiences. The reader should take into account, however, that the effect sizes obtained may be due in part to the use of within-subjects designs.

> ### *Speech and Verbalizations*
> **Music therapy interventions may enhance verbal**
> **communication in Alzheimer's patients. Additional studies**
> **are needed in rehabilitation and other specializations.**

Music therapy interventions (i.e., singing, music reminiscence, active music making) resulted in large improvements in the speech and verbalization behavior of Alzheimer's patients ($k = 4$, $r = .75$). Two studies reported mixed results for speech improvement in rehabilitation patients, and one study reported an increase in verbalization in pediatric patients ($r = .65$). Unfortunately, several rehabilitation studies that examined the effects of music therapy on speech could not be included because of their lack of detailed statistical information. The fact that some of the studies not included did report improvements in speech suggests that additional studies are needed.

Attention and Cognitive Functioning
No interpretations could be made regarding the outcome variable of attention due to the limited number of studies. Music therapy is possibly effective in enhancing cognitive functioning. More studies are needed.

Only two studies examined the effects of music therapy on attention in elderly patients. However, the small total sample size ($N = 22$) prohibits meaningful interpretation.

Several studies ($k = 6$) examined the effects of music therapy or music listening on the cognitive functioning of Alzheimer's patients, and the results of these studies varied widely. Subsequent moderator analysis, however, indicated that music therapy studies ($k = 3$, $r = .42$) led to better and more consistent results that approached statistical significance than music medicine studies ($k = 3$, $r = .13$).

5

AN AGENDA FOR FUTURE RESEARCH

The scope of the current meta-analysis was very broad (comprising 11 medical specializations and 40 categories of outcome variables), and a wealth of information concerning the effects of music medicine or music therapy on health factors of medical patients was discerned. However, of equal importance were findings that suggested issues needing further investigation. In this chapter, the authors have organized these issues into an agenda for future research according to 13 goals. To accomplish this, the findings of the current analysis were synthesized, and a larger, "birds-eye view" perspective was assumed. In addition, governmental health priorities in the United States (e.g., *Healthy People 2010*) were also consulted and incorporated.

The resulting research agenda presented here is intended to be rather general, in that specific topics for future research are not presented in detail. Rather, important areas and methodological strategies for researchers are suggested, and no attempt is made to establish a hierarchy of priorities; all goals are considered equally important. An attempt has been made to create an agenda that is as comprehensive as possible, but it is also clear that these goals can only provide a conceptual framework for future investigations. It is also clear that any attempt at a research agenda will be "a work in progress," changing and being modified as each new study published sheds further light on a particular topic.

Perhaps the most important intended outcome of the current research agenda is to encourage researchers to work collaboratively so that larger research questions may be addressed in a systematic manner. Although it is clear that individual investigators have developed specific "lines of research" wherein they systematically use the results of each study conducted to provide the impetus for the next studies, this does not seem to be case for many researchers. Generally speaking, it appears that future research might well benefit from a more concerted effort among researchers to coordinate approaches, methodologies, outcomes and priorities both throughout medical specializations and between the disciplines of music medicine and music therapy.

> *Goal 1: To clearly distinguish music therapy from music medicine in research endeavors and to increase the amount of music therapy research within all medical specializations.*

Objective A: To actively investigate the influence and components of client-therapist relationship, music and process on research outcomes.

There may be a number of reasons to account for the preponderance of music medicine studies vs. music therapy studies currently appearing in the literature, and the authors can only speculate why this is the case (e.g., lack of opportunities in clinical practice, lack of funding, etc.). Surprising and noteworthy, however, are the studies conducted by music therapists in which music medicine approaches are employed! As music therapy, by definition, involves music, a client-therapist relationship and a therapeutic process, these are essential elements to be incorporated into experimental interventions. Moreover, the results of the current study support the greater effectiveness of music therapy as a treatment intervention as compared to music medicine.

Clinical music therapy interventions are tailored to the individual needs of a client (as determined by assessment), and as such, are difficult to "standardize" across subjects for experimental research purposes (and indeed standardization of treatment protocols is considered a necessity in this research). In contrast, music medicine interventions are much easier to "standardize." In using a limited number of pre-recorded music selections, the music treatment is similar for all subjects receiving treatment.

The individualized nature of music therapy treatment obviously renders music therapy experimental research more difficult to conduct, but certainly not impossible, and a number of researchers have found approaches that allow for individualization of treatment within clearly defined parameters. Specifically, a music therapy treatment method is defined (e.g., GIM) in a manner that is standard for each subject, but which allows flexibility in implementation (e.g., the selection of music or imagery focus used). Moreover, some researchers have predefined a limited number of specific, "standardized" types of music therapy interventions (e.g., those geared towards pain reduction, stress reduction, mood enhancement, etc.) for a particular study, and one or more of these treatments are implemented according to the needs of a research subject during an experimental session. In this way, standardized treatments are defined and implemented, and the subject's individual needs are also addressed. It will be important for future researchers to identify creative strategies such that music therapy treatment may be 'standardized' for a particular study and at the same time may be sufficiently flexible to meet the individual needs of highly vulnerable medical patients.

Objective B: To investigate the effectiveness of a broad range of music therapy approaches, besides receptive.

In implementing music therapy within medical specializations, patients are often physically and emotionally fragile due to illness or medical procedures. For this reason, receptive music therapy experiences that do not require active participation of the patient are often the only available options for treatment. However, for patients whose conditions are not so compromised, a broader range of music therapy interventions is available, i.e., improvisation, song-writing, singing, etc. Although these interventions are used widely in clinical music therapy, they are not sufficiently represented in the medical music therapy research literature, and it is considered essential to investigate their effectiveness, as this is necessary for evidence-based practice.

Thus, it is considered essential: 1) to clearly distinguish and define the parameters of music medicine and music therapy both for clinical practice and in research (including areas where there is an overlap and lack of clear distinction); 2) to continue to determine and contrast the corresponding effectiveness of each approach (as the current meta-analysis has done); 3) to conduct more music therapy studies within all medical specializations; 4) to expand the range of music therapy interventions tested through research; and 5) to develop new music therapy approaches to be investigated. These efforts will serve to enhance the future employment of music therapists in medical settings, especially as research continues to document its greater effectiveness than music medicine. More importantly, however, the needs of medical patients will be addressed in the broadest way possible.

> *Goal 2: To define specific characteristics of the music as well as types of music therapy approaches required for specific therapeutic purposes, e.g., stress reduction, pain management*

Objective A: To identify specific musical elements (rhythm, harmony, melody, timbre, tempo, meter, etc.); instrumentation (vocal versus instrumental, lyrics versus no lyrics, type of instruments); and performance methods (live versus recorded) which affect health parameters of the listener.

In both music medicine as well as receptive music therapy interventions, the nature of the music stimulus is assumed to be of great importance in influencing therapeutic outcomes. However, there is only limited (and dated) foundational research available on this topic, and it appears that the designing and/or selection of music materials for therapeutic purposes is currently more of an "art" than a "science." (Obviously, patient preference is an important factor in selecting music, and this issue will be discussed in conjunction with Goal 4).

The lack of collaboration among researchers is likely a factor contributing to this reality, as there is little similarity in the musical selections used from study to study. Moreover, in far too many studies, researchers fail to even mention the types of music used in the intervention. Therefore, it is difficult to replicate music interventions from study to study, and there is no identifiable repertoire of music selections in various styles that has been tested repeatedly for therapeutic benefits.

Thus, an important goal is the execution of prospective research that identifies if and how there is a relationship between specific, salient musical elements (rhythm, harmony, melody, timbre, tempo, etc) and health benefits. Obviously, this research is complex, as it is indeed difficult to separate out the influence of specific music elements and their effects versus the music gestalt. Likewise, it is extremely difficult to make generalizations about both the elements of music and music gestalt across patients with varying medical conditions, ages and backgrounds. However, it would be important to know, for example, if rhythm and tempo are important musical components for influencing heart rate in cardiac patients, if music lacking harmonic tension is effective in reducing anxiety, if meter influences breathing patterns, etc., etc.

Beyond an examination of these elements, it is also considered essential to investigate if and how music instrumentation influences the listener. For example, are certain instruments more effective in inducing relaxed states in the listener, and conversely, are certain instruments contraindicated for this purpose?

It is also important to examine the effects of instrumental versus vocal music for a variety of therapeutic intents. For example, from a clinical perspective, therapists are aware that the use of vocal music often elicits strong emotional reactions in the listener. If this is the case, how might vocal music detract from pain or facilitate anxiety reduction, for example?

Furthermore, many other questions emerge concerning the inclusion of lyrics in musical stimuli, for example: do existing song lyrics influence various outcomes differentially? Can specific lyrics be created to enhance intended outcomes?

Lastly, aside from the pioneering study of Bailey (1983), there has been little research that compares the effects of live versus pre-recorded music on various health outcomes. This line of research needs to continue.

Obviously, the complexity of music and the interaction of all of these factors render these important research efforts painstaking, and study results may not be easily generalized, if at all. Therefore, it is crucial to determine through research if a certain amount of generalization concerning music selections for specific health benefits is even possible. If this is the case, it would then be essential to: 1) identify through research a set of general parameters that can assist researchers (and clinicians) in making music selections, as well as instrumentation and performance decisions based on evidence, and 2) facilitate a compilation of musical selections that have been tested repeatedly and found to be effective in enhancing various health outcomes.

Objective B: To identify specific music therapy experiences that are most effective in addressing common clinical needs of medical patients, e.g., stress reduction, pain management, mood enhancement, emotional expression, sensory stimulation, etc.

As research concerning the efficacy of music therapy interventions throughout all medical specializations increases (Goal 2), it will be important to compare and analyze the results of various categories of music therapy experiences (receptive, recreative, improvisational, compositional) in addressing both the common and the specialized clinical needs of medical patients. This line of research will help determine which types of experiences are most readily indicated for an array of clinical issues. As there are numerous methods and approaches possible within each of these categories of experiences as well as numerous and diverse clinical issues to be addressed within all of the medical specializations, it is expected that a large number of studies will be needed.

However, these research efforts reflect the core of music therapy practice in medicine, and will contribute most substantially to evidence-based practice.

Goal 3: To investigate more completely music's ability to entrain with biopsychosocial phenomena

The "iso" principle, a foundational concept in music therapy practice, suggests that music can be used to match various psychological states. Once this matching has occurred, a change in the music can also effect a corresponding change in the individual's psychological state.

In the current meta-analytic review, several studies have pointed to the ability of music therapy to entrain with physiological and/or psychological phenomena (e.g., Bradt, 2001; Rider, 1985), and the process of music therapy entrainment, involving both music and resonance by the therapist (Dileo, 1997; Dileo & Bradt, 1999), holds promise for reducing pain. However, earlier, pioneering studies have also supported the idea that music alone can be used to entrain with a range of physiological phenomena, and additional research on this topic needs to occur. For example, it is important to ascertain if rhythm and tempo are more influential than other musical elements in entraining with physiological rhythms (e.g., heart rate, respiration), just as Thaut's research (Thaut, et al., 1993, 1995, 1997, 2002) has shown the effects of rhythmic musical stimuli in structuring and enhancing movement. Are there physiological states or clinical conditions with which music more readily or less readily entrains? Does the emotional presence of the therapist enhance these effects?

Goal 4: To identify specific intra-subject variables that impact on the effectiveness of treatment

Although not investigated directly in many music medicine or music therapy studies, there are numerous intra-subject variables that may influence the effectiveness of treatment. Moreover, these variables are not often reported in descriptions of subjects nor are they assessed as potential covariates. Subject information that tends to be reported more frequently includes: gender, age and music preference (although 32 studies in the current analysis failed to report information on subject preference). Other variables are rarely reported and include subjects' cognitive abilities, musical training, expectations of and attitudes towards the music or music therapy intervention, cultural influences, locus of control, state/trait anxiety (when this is not an outcome measure), personality type(s), spiritual beliefs, acceptance of treatment, severity of illness, etc. All of these factors, and others as well, have the potential to influence study results; several are discussed below.

The inclusion of subjects' genders in published research is standard practice and is not a current concern for this research agenda. However, there is a concern about the paucity of music medicine or music therapy studies focusing on women's health issues in general (aside from medical issues that affect women alone). Currently, there are substantial governmental efforts to examine risk factors and gender differences that render women especially vulnerable to disease (e.g., heart disease), and it is becoming clearer that results of health research performed with male subjects do not apply to women. Furthermore, previous research supports the notion that females and males respond differentially to music medicine or music therapy interventions (e.g., Standley, 2000). It is thus considered essential to: 1) create a line of research in music medicine and music therapy that examines these effects on the range of women's health issues, 2) include equal numbers of male and female subjects in all research (except when the medical condition is gender-specific), and 3) prospectively and routinely assess gender differences in response to music medicine or music therapy interventions.

Subjects' musical backgrounds and training were not routinely assessed in the studies included in the current review, although studies in other clinical areas have indicated that individuals with such training may have differential responses to music when compared to non-trained individuals. One of the difficulties in assessing this variable is defining quantitatively what constitutes "musical training." As individuals may have various educational experiences in music throughout a lifetime (e.g., private music instruction, music theory classes, participation in choirs, etc.), it is challenging to discern the point at which once becomes "musically trained." Unfortunately, researchers may make this determination arbitrarily, as no universal criteria could be found in the literature. For comparison purposes, it is not uncommon for researchers to assess musical responses of music majors vs. non-music majors, as these categorizations are more readily accessible. However, these subject groups are neither relevant nor available for music and medicine research. Thus, a more universal definition of what constitutes "musical training" is needed for research purposes. And because gradations of musical training must be acknowledged, standardized scales may be developed to rate subjects prior to their participation in studies.

In a similar manner, it is often difficult to operationalize what constitutes a subject's music preference within research. Definitions of what is preferred may range from a subject's very favorite musical piece to what he or she dislikes least according to what is offered.

As investigators often attempt to limit and standardize as much as possible the musical stimuli used in their studies, musical selections are often predetermined according to musical styles (e.g., classical, popular, new age, etc.), and participants are asked to select music according to their "preference." In some cases, subjects are permitted to hear the various options prior to making a selection, and in other cases not. As mentioned previously, one may question how reliably and validly the music represents the subject's true "preferred music." Rarely do researchers pretest the music with subjects to determine if indeed they like it. Similarly, posttests are not often used to determine subjects' satisfaction with what has been heard. The use of these additional measures might enhance research designs.

Occasionally, investigators ask subjects to bring their favorite music to be used in a study. Although this procedure may more accurately make use of a subject's true musical preference, there are a number of inherent concerns as well. When doing this, it is obvious that the musical stimuli used in the study will be far from "standardized." Also, the qualities of the music that subjects select as "preferred" may be inconsistent with the intent of the experimental treatment, e.g., relaxation. Furthermore, subjects may select music that elicits vivid memories and strong emotional reactions, both positive and negative, and these reactions may confound the intent of the experimental treatment.

In addition, a subject's familiarity with music often interacts with music preference. For example, it is obvious that it may be contradictory to "prefer" music or musical styles that one has not yet heard. Therefore, it is important for researchers to assess familiarity with the music used prior to the study. Doing this will also provide a necessary ethical safeguard and reduce risks to subjects, i.e., in determining if the music used in the study elicits strong memories and emotional reactions in the subject prior to implementation. Lastly, besides the aforementioned reasons given for the pre-testing of music stimuli, this process may help more clearly assess in advance if the music stimuli in general are consistent with the study intent, e.g., if subjects rate the music to be used as "relaxing," etc.

Various personality factors/personality have been associated with susceptibility to as well as survival from illness in the behavioral medicine literature. It is becoming more evident that psychological states (e.g., depression), as well as personality types and coping styles, have some predictive validity for one's health and recovery. As this extensive literature holds enormous implications for music medicine and music therapy research, it is quite surprising that these findings are not utilized more frequently or given adequate consideration in the conceptualization and design of studies. It will be important for future research to investigate these factors prospectively and as covariates in the analysis of research results.

Subjects' responses to music may be strongly influenced by their cultures. When defined broadly, culture may include: gender, age, disability, language, religion/spiritual orientation, ethnicity, socioeconomic status, sexual orientation, indigenous heritage and national origin (Dileo, 2000). Subjects' cultures are rarely assessed prospectively or as a covariate in music and medicine research.

Given current national priorities to address inequities in access to healthcare due to cultural variables (e.g., *Healthy People 2010*), it is of paramount importance for future research to investigate how music medicine or music therapy interventions may most effectively be implemented with medical patients from non-dominant cultures. It is likely that "traditional" interventions will need to be modified and new approaches developed to meet the physical, emotional, social, spiritual and musical needs of these patients (Dileo & Magill, 2005; Dileo & Starr, 2005). As an example, the experience and expression of pain is often culturally dependent. Music medicine and music therapy research interventions aimed at pain reduction in subjects from different cultures will likely result in idiosyncratic findings, if subjects' cultures are not given a priori considerations in designing interventions and selecting measurement tools.

> ***Goal 5: To identify social context variables that may impact on the effectiveness of treatment and to investigate the influences of music medicine and music therapy in enhancing aspects of social relatedness.***

Although rarely investigated in music medicine and music therapy research, a number of variables within subjects' social contexts may influence the effectiveness of experimental interventions. These variables include but are not limited to: relationships with family and caregivers, relationships with medical staff, attitudes toward treatment, satisfaction with treatment, perceptions regarding social support, etc. As these factors may confound treatment results, it is considered important that they be assessed and controlled for in designing research.

Conversely, there is vastly insufficient research on these factors as potential outcome variables for music medicine and music therapy research. Whereas a large body of literature has underscored the diverse health benefits of subjects' perceived social support and social relatedness (e.g., in preventing and in surviving from a range of illnesses), much of the current published research in the area of music and medicine is not conceptualized accordingly, i.e., it does not acknowledge or assess these potential benefits for health directly. Moreover, knowledge concerning the health benefits of social support should influence **all** music therapy research undertaken even outside of medicine.

Furthermore, research on the effects of music medicine or music therapy on patients' caregivers (family and staff) is insufficient to date. Future studies may well suggest the positive benefits of these interventions in easing the stress and demands of caregiving, in improving the health of caregivers, and in improving the subsequent quality of caregiving to the patient.

> ***Goal 6: To utilize a variety of research paradigms as well as more rigorous research designs to best understand the effects of music medicine or music therapy interventions.***

Although the research studies used in the current review were all quantitative in nature, the authors strongly emphasize the urgent need for and undisputed value of qualitative studies in music medicine and music therapy. Because it is quite clear that quantitative research is capable of providing only a portion of the information needed by clinical practitioners in these areas, findings from qualitative studies are sorely needed. The authors view these two research paradigms as complementary; lingering research questions that emerge from quantitative research may often be addressed through qualitative research, and visa versa. Qualitative research provides the means through which investigators may answer a host of questions, for example: What is the experience of music listening by patients awaiting surgery? How do music therapists utilize therapeutic presence at the hospital bedside? How do patients describe their pain in musical terms within the entrainment process? What is the meaning of the songwriting process among neurologically impaired patients, their families and their music therapists?

No matter which approach is used in music and medicine research, rigorous research designs are required. In quantitative research, the randomized double-blind control trial (RCT) is often considered the "gold standard" by medical researchers. Although this design may be difficult to execute routinely in music therapy research for a number of reasons, it may be a standard to which researchers aspire in the future. Only fifty percent of the studies used in this review were randomized trials.

For the current review, within-subjects designs were used much more frequently in music therapy research (51.8%) than in music medicine research (19.37%). Also, as noted previously, within-subjects designs in the present study yielded significantly higher mean effect sizes than did randomized designs. In addition, the percentage of within-subjects designs used (out of the total number of studies) also varied according to the medical specialization (Table 82).

Table 82
Percentage of Within-Subjects Designs According to
Medical Specialization

Surgery 2%
Cardiology/ICU: 28.5%
Cancer/Terminal Illness/AIDS: 36.8%
Fetal: 75%
General Hospital: 0%
Neonatology: 41.2%
OB/GYN: 14.3 %
Pediatrics: 9%
Dental: 16.7%
Alzheimer's: 73%
Rehabilitation: 44.4%

There may be compelling reasons for music therapists *not* to employ RCT designs, and these reasons will undoubtedly vary. Sometimes the ethical issue of withholding treatment, or offering no treatment may dissuade researchers from using this design. Also, for medical populations, it may be quite difficult to obtain informed consent when subjects are made aware that they have an equal chance of being assigned to a control group. Many of the subjects used in this research are quite ill and are undergoing various stressful and/or invasive medical procedures; they may not be inclined to participate in studies where there is a good chance that there will be no direct benefit to them. This is especially the case with end of life patients, i.e., patients' time is extremely limited and valuable and not to be wasted as a control subject. For these reasons, it is becoming increasingly common that control subjects receive some type of contact (i.e., attentional control) with the experimenter in whatever non-confounding form this might take (casual conversation, etc.), and potential effects of this contact are assessed.

For future meta-analytic reviews, it would be important to increase the number of randomized designs and various types of these used in music therapy studies across all medical specializations.

In addition, it is especially critical for researchers for include a more detailed reporting of statistics, especially when no significant effects are found (rather than using the blanket statement, "no significant differences were found"). In doing so, effect size calculations could be more specific regarding the lack of effect, and this would likely increase the mean effect sizes reported. More specifically, it is important that the researcher reports: (a) type of study design, (b) level of randomization, (c) total sample size as well as sample size of *each* group, (d) means and associated standard deviations, (e) statistics that compare the pre-posttest changes of the experimental group with the pre-posttest changes of the control group, (f) detailed statistical information, i.e., t-value, F-value, etc. and p-values (the exact p-value should always be provided).

In the current review, only a limited number of potential moderator variables could be examined because of the inconsistency in the reporting of this information across studies. In future research, it is essential that researchers provide additional information on variables, such as: subjects' ages, genders, ethnicity, musical background, emotional state, personality traits/factors, level of social support, severity of illness, attitude towards (music therapy) treatment, satisfaction with (music therapy) treatment, type of music, subjects' music preferences, music therapy intervention, so that the effects of these variables can be analyzed. It is realized that it may not be feasible for all researchers to collect all of this information for all subjects in all studies. At the same time, the authors stress the necessity of conducting foundational research to determine the influence of these variables on music therapy outcomes in medical populations. Such research may facilitate the identification of a hierarchy of confounding variables for specific outcomes or medical specializations.

> **Goal 7: To investigate directly various treatment delivery specifications and their comparative effectiveness**

As music medicine and music therapy researchers design studies, questions typically arise, such as: how much music listening/music therapy is needed to be effective? How many interventions are required? How long should the interventions be? When should they be offered? Where should interventions be offered? Is there a satiation effect?

These are not unfamiliar or unusual questions, because there are no uniform procedures available that are associated with optimal effects, moreover there have been few studies that address these issues directly according to the intended outcome variable(s). Obviously, the answers to these questions cannot and should not be universal, considering the great range of medical patients' needs. However, it would be extremely helpful for this information to be forthcoming in the literature in the form of guidelines for research and clinical practice.

> **Goal 8: To investigate the effectiveness of music listening or music therapy alone versus its combination with other approaches for a variety of research outcomes.**

In music therapy practice, it is not uncommon for receptive music experiences (either using live or taped music) to be combined with other, traditional approaches, especially in stress or pain management interventions. For example, music is often combined with progressive muscle relaxation, autogenic techniques, massage, imagery, low-frequency stimulation and/or suggestion. Occasionally, research studies have compared the effectiveness of these approaches alone and in combination, e.g., music alone, progressive muscle relaxation alone and music + progressive muscle relaxation and control. These designs are considered optimal, as conclusions about the effects of each intervention can then be made and compared.

From a research perspective, it is problematic, however, when music is combined with another type of intervention (previously tested or not) and these results are compared only with a control group or control condition. In these cases, it is impossible to draw any conclusions, because either of the interventions or their combination may be responsible for the obtained outcome.

At the same time, it is not recommended that multiple experimental groups be used without having a large enough sample sizes for each group (and the number of subjects needed should be determined by a power analysis). In the current review, music therapy studies, in general, tended to employ smaller sample sizes (min. $N = 5$, max. $N = 80$, mean $N = 24.78$ ($SD = 17.07$) than music medicine studies (min. $N = 9$, max. $N = 500$, mean $N = 54.28$ ($SD = 54.28$), and this factor invariably reduces statistical power.

From a clinical perspective (as discussed in conjunction with Goal 1), the range of methods and approaches used in music therapy has not been tested with medical patients. Furthermore, new approaches are continuing to be developed and tested. There is a pressing need to identify and test the effects of music therapy interventions that are consistent with the unique skills and training of music therapists, (i.e., the use of live music, active engagement of the patient and therapeutic presence), especially for common clinical problems such as anxiety and pain reduction. Approaches, as described above, that may rely on pre-recorded music and the use of traditional verbal relaxation inductions, may be implemented by professionals from other disciplines, and these practices do not require specialized training in music therapy. Addressing and defining the methods that are unique to music therapy, therefore, is essential in preserving the integrity of the discipline and its professional training.

**Goal 9: To identify, through collaboration with medical professionals,
the most significant and meaningful outcome variables
to be studied for each clinical specialization**

Objective A: To determine the most significant outcome variables within each clinical specialization.

In the research studies used in the current review, numerous outcome variables were identified (N=180). This was expected due to the range of clinical issues/symptoms present among the 11 medical specializations. Although common clinical issues are present in many different types of medical patients, e.g., pain, anxiety and mood disturbance, there are also unique problems to be addressed within the various specializations.

In spite of this current number of outcome variables, this list is certainly not exhaustive, and it is expected that many additional variables will need to be explored in future studies. Input from medical personnel is thus required to assist music therapy researchers in identifying the most significant and meaningful outcome variables for patients to be tested in studies. For example, heart rate variability is a significant indicator of cardiac health and illness, and the effects of music therapy on this variable will need further investigation.

Objective B: To continue to assess the outcomes that appear to be influenced significantly and consistently by music medicine or music therapy interventions within and across medical specializations and to determine the generalizability and predictability of these effects.

A number of outcome variables were identified in the current review that were found to be influenced significantly and consistently by music medicine or music therapy interventions. Recommendations for future research concerning these and other symptom-level variables have already been made throughout this book, and these will not be repeated here. Thus, it is essential in the future to determine the consistency and generalizability of these effects within and among medical specializations.

In addition, there is a need to identify the most sensitive, reliable and valid measurement tools in detecting the effects of music medicine or music therapy treatments (physiological, psychological, cognitive, social, behavioral, spiritual, etc.) according to clinical population. In the current review, a variety of measurement tools were employed to assess the same outcome. For example, in measuring treatment effects on anxiety, a number of studies employed the *State-Trait Anxiety Inventory*, whereas a number of studies used other, diverse measures. When divergent measures are used, effect size calculations are more difficult to obtain and must be interpreted more cautiously. However, when multiple researchers use the same outcome measures, the effect size calculations yield more conclusive findings, and generalizations are more accurately made. It goes without saying that standardized outcome measures should be employed in future research whenever possible.

Also, it is not uncommon for researchers to assess outcomes of music medicine or music therapy treatments in several domains simultaneously (e.g., physiological, psychological, social) or using various types of measurement tools (e.g., physiological recordings, self-reports, behavioral observations). It is also not uncommon for disparate and sometimes conflicting results to be obtained among these measures. Thus, for future research, it will be important to determine which of these measures can provide the most reliable, valid and sensitive indications of the intended outcome.

Objective C: To continue to investigate the interrelationships among various outcome measures.

From a biopsychosocial perspective, close interrelationships exist among physiological, psychological, cognitive, behavioral, social, and spiritual aspects of the individual, and changes in one domain inevitably influence changes in the other domains. Although researchers in music and medicine may well acknowledge this phenomenon, within the current body of literature, these interrelationships have not been investigated prospectively, as they have been in the behavioral medicine literature. Therefore, it is imperative that investigators consider these relationships in designing and implementing future studies. In doing so, many significant questions will emerge. For example: Is there a relationship between mood changes achieved through songwriting and subjects' immune functioning? Is there a relationship between the improved social support achieved through group music therapy and cardiac function in post-MI patients? Is there a relationship between the anxiety reductions achieved through music improvisation and improved medication compliance in AIDS patients? The answers to these and many other similar questions will undoubtedly advance the status of music therapy in integrative medicine.

Objective D: To investigate more fully the effects of music medicine or music therapy on outcome measures that impact on cost-effectiveness issues.

Within the current review, there were only a few studies that addressed cost-effectiveness issues of music therapy or music medicine interventions. As these issues directly impact on employment and reimbursement practices, a line of research on these topics is urgently needed. Thus, future investigations will need to assess the costs of music medicine or music therapy interventions as compared to costs associated with: hospital stay, the length of time in intensive care units, recovery time, medication use, anesthesia use, success of medical tests and procedures, time commitments from other medical personnel, etc. In addition, the effects of music medicine or music therapy on patient satisfaction and compliance with treatment are also critical topics for future research. Finally, as mentioned previously, future researchers should investigate the effects of music therapy or music medicine on medical staff performance (e.g., during surgery), on staff burnout, on staff attendance, and on general staff satisfaction.

> ### Goal 10: To investigate the effects of music medicine or music therapy on important medical conditions which have received little or no attention in the literature.

Quite obvious in the current review is the limited number of studies (or complete absence of studies) concerning the effects of music medicine or music therapy on symptoms associated with number of common medical conditions. These conditions are also priorities in national health initiatives and include: diabetes, asthma and other respiratory disorders, blood pressure disorders, HIV/AIDS, endocrine and metabolic disorders, women's health issues, pre-natal care, and the range of autoimmune diseases (arthritis, lupus, multiple sclerosis, etc.). Research in these areas and others is urgently needed.

There are many medical tests and procedures during which patients' experiences may be potentially enhanced by the use of music medicine or music therapy, and these have yet to be studied, or have not been studied extensively (e.g., in dentistry): for example, donor insemination procedures, various endoscopy procedures and many others.

Additional research is warranted concerning the immediate and long-term biochemical effects of music medicine or music therapy interventions in medical patients. Although some pioneering research has been accomplished, future research should examine various outcomes such as immune functioning, endogenous hormones and neurotransmitters.

Noticeably absent are studies involving populations with combined psychiatric/medical disorders or developmental disabilities/medical disorders. Individuals who suffer from these complex problems have unique treatment needs, and current research findings in music medicine or music therapy may not generalize readily to these populations. For example, there is a pressing need for specialized music medicine or music therapy interventions for developmentally disabled individuals undergoing medical procedures.

Although not included in the current review, studies concerning brain processing of music provide critical foundational information upon which to base future. More specifically, future studies will be needed to examine how music is processed, and the brain mechanisms involved, especially for patients with various medical conditions and neurological disorders.

> ### Goal 11: To investigate the long-term and developmental effects of music medicine or music therapy interventions.

Few studies in music medicine or music therapy have included data concerning the long-term or developmental effects of these treatments. It is obvious that this information is needed, in spite of the inherent demands and difficulties of this type of research (e.g., funding, subject attrition, etc.).

Whereas a number of the studies in this review address short-term clinical conditions (e.g., medical procedures), it is indeed possible that the effects of music medicine or music therapy interventions may be ongoing. For example, it would be very significant to determine: Does music therapy influence the long-term immune status of cancer patients? Does music therapy influence the long-term physical or cognitive development of premature infants? Does music therapy slow the progression of Alzheimer's disease? It is impossible to overestimate the potential implications of these and other studies for these two disciplines.

Goal 12: To investigate the impact of music therapy or music medicine on the larger and most significant health issues.

The time is approaching for researchers to begin to study the effects of music therapy or music medicine on the larger and more critical current health issues. If successful, these studies will undoubtedly revolutionize the disciplines and ensure their inclusion as necessary modalities within health care. Perhaps it is time to envision some possible topics:

> ➢ Does music therapy influence the length of survival from illness and how?
> ➢ Does music therapy significantly influence medical patients' quality of life?
> ➢ Can music therapy be used as a primary (as opposed to a complementary) treatment for some medical conditions, e.g., pain?
> ➢ Does music medicine routinely enhance the success of and patient satisfaction with medical tests and procedures?
> ➢ Does music therapy mediate the effects of other health deterrents (e.g., lifestyle)?
> ➢ Does music therapy significantly improve the course of illness?
> ➢ Do music medicine or music therapy significantly reduce costs associated with medical care?
> ➢ Etc. Etc....the list goes on and on.

Goal 13: To investigate the potential role of music therapy or music medicine in the prevention of illness.

There are few, if any, studies concerning the potential roles of music therapy or music medicine in preventing health problems and subsequent illness, and this topic will be a critical one for future investigators with many potential ramifications for these fields. However, collaboration among researchers within other clinical populations (besides medicine) will be required to accomplish this, and an overarching biopsychosocial framework will need to be adopted. More specifically, music therapy researchers will need to examine the potential health benefits (immediate and long-term) for **all** research interventions with **all** clinical populations and assess these potential outcomes prospectively.

For example, it will be important to determine: What is the impact of music therapy treatment for the remediation of psychiatric symptoms (e.g., depression, anxiety, psychotic illness) on the prevention of future illness? What is the impact of music therapy aimed at enhancing social integration on the prevention of future illness? What is the impact of music therapy aimed at enhancing patient coping skills on the prevention of future illness? In essence, researchers will need to take into consideration the potential impact of **all** music therapy interventions on subjects' immediate and future health status.

In addition, it will be important in the future to assess the effectiveness of music medicine or music therapy in addressing common health risk factors (as identified by governmental agencies) (Table 83).

Table 83
Health Risk Factors

Lifestyle Issues	Lack of Exercise
Excessive weight	Smoking
Alcohol/Substance Abuse	Lack of Sleep
Irresponsible Sexual Behavior	Lack of Prenatal Care
Excessive Stress	Lack of Coping Skills
No Health Screenings	Avoidance of Medical
Lack of Compliance with Medical	Treatment
Treatment	

Concluding Remarks

It is with great optimism for the future that the authors conclude this book. The meta-analytic results obtained are most encouraging for music medicine and music therapy practitioners alike, and indeed for the entire music therapy profession. At the same time, there is much more research to be accomplished in the future, and it is hoped that the agenda provided will serve to guide some of this work. At times the sheer volume of research that needs to be done can feel overwhelming, however, it is important to temper this with a realization of how far the disciplines have come in recent times, and to embrace all that is currently known (as well as what is still not known).

Most importantly, it is hoped that the contents of this book will make a difference for the medical patients we serve, as this is what will always matter most and continue to be the top priority.

REFERENCES

Abbott, C. M. (1995). The effect of music therapy on the perceived quality of life of patients with terminal illness in a hospice setting. Unpublished master's thesis. Western Michigan University. Michigan. (Cancer/Terminal Illness/AIDS)

Aitken, J. C., Wilson, S., Coury, D., & Moursi, A. M. (2002). The effect of music distraction on pain, anxiety and behavior in pediatric dental patients. *Pediatric Dentistry, 24*(2), 114-118. (Dental)

Albert, R. E. (2001). The effect of guided imagery and music on pain and anxiety during laceration repair. Unpublished Doctoral Dissertation. Case Western Reserve University, Cleveland, OH. (General Hospital)

Allen, K., Golden, L. H., Izzo, J. L., Jr., Ching, M.L., Forrest, A., Niles, C.R., Niswander, P.R., & Barlow, J.C. (2001). Normalization of hypertensive responses during ambulatory surgical stress by perioperative music. *Psychosomatic Medicine, 63,* 487-492. (Surgery)

Ammon, K. (1968). The effects of music on children in respiratory distress. ANA Clinical Sessions, 127-134. (Pediatrics)

Anderson, R. A., & Baron, R. S. (1991). Distraction, control and dental stress. *Journal of Applied Social Psychology, 21,* 156-171. (Dental)

Angus, J. E. & Faux, S. (1989). The effect of music on adult postoperative patients' pain during a nursing procedure. In S. G. Funk, E. M. Tornquist, M.T. Champagne, L. A. Copp, & R. A. Wiese (Eds). *Key Apects of Comfort. Management of pain, fatigue and nausea.* NY: Springer Publishing Company. (Surgery)

Arts, S. E., Abu-Saad, H. H., Champion, G. D., Crawford, M. R., Fisher, R. J., Juniper, K. H., & Ziegler, J. B. (1994). Age-related response to Lidocaine-Prilocaine (EMLA) Emulsion and effect of music distraction on the pain of intravenous cannulation. *Pediatrics, 93,* 797-801. (Surgery)

Ashida, S. (2000). The effect of reminiscence music therapy on changes in depressive symptoms in elderly persons with dementia. *Journal of Music Therapy, 37,* 183-195. (Alzheimer's)

Augustin, O. & Hains, A. (1996). Effect of music on ambulatory surgery patients' preoperative anxiety. *AORN Journal, 63*(4), 753-758. (Surgery)

Barnason, Zimmerman, & Nieveen (1995). The effects of music interventions on anxiety in the patient after coronary artery bypass grafting. *Heart Lung, 24*(2), 124-132. (Surgery)

Barrera, M. E., Rykov, M. H., Doyle, S. L. (2002). The effects of interactive music therapy on hospitalized children with cancer: A pilot study. *Psycho-Oncology, 11,* 379-388. (Cancer/Terminal Illness/AIDS)

Beck, S. L. (1991). The therapeutic use of music for cancer-related pain. *Oncology Nursing Forum, 18,* 1327-1337. (Cancer/Terminal Illness/AIDS)

Blankfield, R. P., Zyzanski, S. J., Flocke, S. A., Alemagno, A., & Scheurman, K. (1995). Taped therapeutic suggestions and taped music as adjuncts in the care of coronary-artery bypass patients. *American Journal of Clinical Hypnosis, 37*(3), 32-42. (Surgery)

Bolwerk, C. (1990). Effects of relaxing music on state therapy in myocardial infarction patients. *Critical Nurse Quarterly, 13*, 63-72. (Cardiology/ICU)

Bonny, H. (1983). Music listening for intensive coronary care units: A pilot project. *Music Therapy, 3*, 4-16. (Cardiology/ICU)

Brackbill, Y., Adams, G., Crowell, D., & Gray, M. L. (1966). Arousal level in neonates and preschool children under continuous auditory stimulation. *Journal of Experimental Child Psychology, 4*, 178-188. (Neonatology)

Bradt, J. (2001). The effects of music entrainment on postoperative pain perception in pediatric patients. Unpublished doctoral dissertation. Temple University, Philadelphia, PA. (Pediatrics)

Broscious, S. (1999). Music: an intervention for pain during chest tube removal after open heart surgery. *American Journal of Critical Care, 8*(6), 410-415. (Surgery)

Brotons, M. & Koger, S. M. (2000). The impact of music therapy on language functioning in dementia. *Journal of Music Therapy, 37*(3), 183-195. (Alzheimer's)

Brotons, M., & Pickett-Cooper, P. K. (1996). The effects of music therapy intervention on agitation behaviors of Alzheimer's disease patient's. *Journal of Music Therapy, 33*(1), 2-18. (Alzheimer's)

Burke, M. (1997). Effects of physioacoustic intervention on pain management of postoperative gynecological patients. In T. Wigram & C.Dileo (Eds.), *Music vibration and health*. Cherry Hill, NJ: Jeffrey Books. (Surgery)

Burns, S. J., Harbuz, M. S., Hucklebridge, F., & Bunt, L. (2001). A pilot study into the therapeutic effects of music therapy at a cancer help center. Alternative Therapies in Health & Medicine, 7(1), 48-56. (Cancer/Terminal Illness/AIDS)

Butt, M. L. & Kisilevsky, B. S. (2000). Music modulates behaviour of premature infants following heel lance. *Canadian Journal of Nursing Research, 31*(4), 17-39. (Neonatology)

Cadigan, M. E., Caruso, N. A., Haldeman, S. M., McNamara, M. E., Noyes, D. A., Spadafora, M. A., & Carroll, D. L. (2001). The effects of music on cardiac patients on bed rest. *Progress in Cardiovascular Nursing, 16*, 5-13. (Cardiology/ICU)

Caine, J. (1991). The effects of music on the selected stress behaviors, weight, caloric and formula intake and length of hospital stay of premature and low birth weight neonates in a newborn intensive care unit. *Journal of Music Therapy, 28*, 180-192. (Neonatology)

Calovini, B. S. (1993). The effect of participation in one music therapy session on state anxiety in hospice patients. Unpublished master's thesis. Case Western Reserve University, Cleveland, OH. (Cancer/Terminal Illness/AIDS)

Cassileth, B. R., Vickers, A. J., & Magill, L. A. (2003). Music therapy for mood disturbance during hospitalization for autologous stem cell transplantation: A randomized controlled trial. *Cancer, 98*(12), 2723-2726. (Cancer/Terminal Illness/AIDS)

Cassidy, J. W. & Standley, J. W. (1995). The effect of music listening on physiological responses of premature infants in the NICU. *Journal of Music Therapy, 32*, 208-227. (Neonatology)

Cepeda, M. S., Diaz, J. E., Hernandez, V., Daza, E., & Carr, D. B. (1998). Music does not reduce alfentanil requirement during patient-controlled analgesia (PCA) use in extracorporeal shock wave lithotripsy for renal stones. *Journal of Pain and Symptom Management, 16*, 382-387. (General Hospital)

Chapman, J. S. (1978). The relationship between auditory stimulation and gross motor activity of short-gestation infants. *Research in nursing and health, 1*, 29-36. (Neonatology)

Chapman, J. S. (1979). Influence of varied stimuli on development of motor patterns in premature infants. In G. C. Anderson & B. Raff (Eds). *Newborn behavioral organization: Nursing research and implications* (pp.61-80). New York: Liss. (Neonatology)

Chetta, H. D. (1981). The effect of music and desensitization on preoperative anxiety in children. *Journal of Music Therapy, 18*(2), 74-87. (Surgery)

Chlan, L. L. (1995). Psychophysiologic responses of mechanically ventilated patients to music: A pilot study. *American Journal of Critical Care, 4*(3), 233-238. (Cardiology/ICU)

Chlan, L. L.(1998). Effectiveness of a music therapy intervention on relaxation and anxiety for patients receiving ventilatory assistance. *Heart and Lung, 27*(3), 169-176. (Cardiology/ICU)

Clair, A. A. (1994). The effect of no music, stimulative background music, and sedative background music on agitated behaviors in persons with severe dementia. *Activities, Adaptation and Aging, 19*(4), 61-70. (Alzheimer's)

Clair, A. A. (1996). The effect of singing on alert responses in persons with late state dementia. *Journal of Music Therapy, 33*, 234-247. (Alzheimer's)

Clair, A. A. (1997). The effects of music therapy on interactions between family caregivers and their care receivers with late stage dementia. *Journal of Music Therapy, 34*, 148-164. (Alzheimer's)

Clark, M. E., Lipe, A. W., & Bilbrey, M. (1998). Use of music the decrease aggressive behaviors in people with dementia. *Journal of Gerontological Nursing, 24*(7), 10-17. (Alzheimer's)

Clark, M. E., McCorkle, R. R., & Williams, S. B. (1981). Music therapy assisted labor and delivery. Journal of Music Therapy, 18(2), 88-100.(OB/GYN)

Cohen, J. (1977). Statistical power analysis for the behavioral sciences (2nd ed.). New York: Academic Press.

Cohen, N., & Ford, J. (1995). The effect of musical cues on the non-purposive speech of persons with aphasia. *Journal of Music Therapy, 32*, 46-57. (Rehabilitation)

Cohen, N., & Masse, R. (1993). The application of singing and rhythmic instruction as a therapeutic intervention for persons with neurogenic communication disorders. *Journal of Music Therapy, 30*, 81-89. (Rehabilitation)

Coleman, J. M., Pratt, R. R., Stoddar, R. A., Gerstmann, D. R., & Abel, H. (1998). The effects of male and female singing and speaking voices on selected physiological and behavioral measures of premature infants in the intensive care unit. International Journal of Arts Medicine, 5(8), 4-11. (Neonatology)

Collins, S. & Kuck, K. (1991). Music therapy in the neonatal intensive care unit. *Neonatal Network, 9*(6), 23-26. (Neonatology)

Colt, H. G., Powers, A., Shanks, T. G. (1999). Effect of music on state anxiety scores in patients undergoing fiberoptic bronchoscopy. *Chest, 116*(3), 819-824. (General Hospital)

Corah, N., Gale, E., Pace, L. & Seyrek, S. (1981). Relaxation and musical programming as means of reducing psychological stress during dental procedures. *Journal of the American Dental Association, 103*, 232-234. (Dental)

Cordobes, T. K. (1997). Group songwriting as a method for developing group cohesion for HIV-seropositive adult patients with depression. *Journal of Music Therapy, 34*(1), 46-67. (Cancer/Terminal Illness/AIDS)

Cruise, C. J., Chung. F., Yogendran, S., &Little, D. (1997). Music increases satisfaction in elderly outpatients undergoing cataract surgery. *Canadian Journal of Anaesthesia, 44*(1), 43-48. (Surgery)

Curtis, S. (1986). The effect of music on pain relief and relaxation of the terminally ill. *Journal of Music Therapy, 23*, 10-24. (Cancer/Terminal Illness/AIDS)

Daub, D., & Kirschner-Hermanns, R. (1988). Reduction of pre-operative anxiety. [Verminderung der preoperative angst]. *Anaesthetist, 37*, 594-597. (Surgery)

Davila, J. M., & Menendez, J. (1986). Relaxing effects of music in dentistry for mentally handicapped patients. *Special Care in Dentistry, 6*(1), 18-21. (Dental)

Davis, C. A. (1992). The effects of music and basic relaxation instruction on pain and anxiety of women undergoing in-office gynecological procedures. *Journal of Music Therapy, 29*, 202-216. (OB/GYN)

Davis- Rollans, C. & Cunningham, S. (1987). Physiologic responses of coronary care patients to selected music. *Heart and Lung, 16*, 370-378. (Cardiology/ICU)

Dileo, C., & Bradt, J. (2005). Meta-analysis. In: B. Wheeler (Ed.), *Music Therapy Research* (pp.282-292). Gilsum, NH: Barcelona Publishers.

Dubois, J. M, Bartter, T., & Pratter, M. R. (1995). Music improves patient comfort level during outpatient bronchoscopy. *Chest, 108*(1), 129-130. (General Hospital)

Durham, L. & Collins, M. (1986). The effects of music as a conditioning aid in prepared childbirth education. *Journal of Obstetric, Gynecological and Neonatal Nursing, 15*(3), 268-270. (OB/GYN)

Durlak, J. A., Meerson, I., & Foster, C. (2003). Meta-analysis. In J. Thomas & M. Hersen (Eds.), *Understanding research in clinical and counseling psychology* (pp. 243–270). Mahwah, NJ: Lawrence Erlbaum Associates.

Elche, K., & Lavelle, E. A. (1998). Effects of music and massage on dyspnea and peak respiratory flow rate in children with asthma receiving routine beta-adrenergic nebulizations. Unpublished doctoral dissertation. University of Minnesota, Minnesota. (Pediatrics)

Elliot, D. (1994). The effects of music and muscle relaxation on patient anxiety in a coronary care unit. *Heart and Lung Journal of Critical Care, 23*(1), 27-35. (Cardiology/ICU)

Elm, D., Madill, H. & Warren, S. (1998). The effects of auditory stimuli on functional performance among cognitively impaired elderly. *Canadian Journal of Occupational Therapy, 65*(1), 30-36. (Alzheimer's)

Evans, M. M. & Rubio, P. A. (1994). Music: a diversionary therapy. *Today Or-Nurse, 16*(4), 17-22. (Surgery)

Ezzone, S., Baker, C., Rosselet, R., & Terepka, E. (1998). Music as an adjunct to antiemetic therapy. *Oncology Nurses Forum, 25*, 1551-1555. (Cancer/Terminal Illness/AIDS)

Foster, N. A. & Valentine, E. R. (2001). The effect of auditory stimulation on autobiographical recall in dementia. *Experimental Aging Research, 27*, 215-228. (Alzheimer's)

Fowler, K. S., Lander, J. R. (1987). Management of injection pain in children. *Pain, 30*(2), 169-175. (Pediatrics)

Frank, J. M. (1985). The effects of music therapy and guided visual imagery on chemotherapy-induced nausea and vomiting. *Oncology Nursing Forum, 12*(5), 47-52. (Cancer/Terminal Illness/AIDS)

Froehlich, M. A. (1984). A comparison of the effect of music therapy and medical play therapy on the verbalization behavior of pediatric patients. *Journal of Music Therapy, 21*, 126-132. (Pediatrics)

Gaberson, K. B. (1991). The effect of humorous distraction on preoperative anxiety. A pilot study. *AORN Journal, 54*(6), 1258-1264. (Surgery)

Gerdner, L. A. (2000). Effects of individualized versus classical ""relaxation"" music on the frequency of agitation in elderly persons with Alzheimer's disease and related disorders. *International Psychogeriatrics, 12*(1), 49-65. (Alzheimer's)

Goddaer, J. & Abraham, I. L. (1994). Effects of relaxing music on agitation during meals among nursing home residents with severe cognitive impairment. *Archives of Psychiatric Nursing, 8*(3), 150-158. (Alzheimer's)

Gold, C. (2004). The use of effect sizes in music therapy research. Music Therapy Perspectives, *22*, 91–95.

Gold, C., Heldal, T. O., Dahle, T., & Wigram, T. (in press). Music therapy for schizophrenia and schizophrenia-like illnesses (Cochrane Review), *The Cochrane Library, 2, 2005*. Chichester, UK: John Wiley & Sons, Ltd.

Gold, C., Voracek, M., & Wigram, T. (2004). Effects of music therapy for children and adolescents with psychopathology: A meta-analysis. *Journal of Child Psychology* and Psychiatry and Allied Disciplines, 45, 1054–1063.

Gold, C., & Wigram, T. (2005). Music therapy for autistic spectrum disorder. [Protocol]. *Cochrane Database of Systematic Reviews,* Issue 1.

Goff L. C., Pratt R. R., & Madrigal J. L. (1997). Music listening and S-IgA levels in patients undergoing a dental procedure. *International Journal of Arts Medicine, 5*(2), 22-26. (Dental)

Good, M. (1995). A comparison of the effects of jaw relaxation and music on postoperative pain. *Nursing Research, 44*(1), 52-57. (Surgery)

Good, M., Anderson, G. C., Stanton-Hicks, M., Grass, J. A., & Makii, M. (2002). Relaxation and music reduce pain after gynecologic surgery. *Pain Management Nursing, 3*(2), 61-70. (Surgery)

Good, M., & Chin, C. C. (1998). The effects of western music on postoperative pain in Taiwan. *Kaosiung Journal of Medical Science, 14*, 94-103. (Surgery)

Grasso, M. C., Button, B. M., Allison, D., & Sawyer, S. M. (2000). Benefits of music therapy as an adjunct to chest physiotherapy in infants and toddlers with cystic fibrosis. *Pediatric Pulmonology, 29*(5), 371-381. (Pediatrics)

Groene, R. W. (1993). Effectiveness of music therapy intervention with individuals having senile dementia of the Alzheimer's type. *Dissertation Abstracts International, 53* (10A). (Alzheimer's)

Hall, J.A., & Rosenthal R. (1995). Interpreting and evaluating meta-analysis. *Evauation & the Health Profession, 18*(4), 393-407.

Hamel, W. J. (2001). The effects of music intervention on anxiety in the patient waiting for cardiac catheterization. *Intensive and Critical Care Nursing, 17*, 279-285 (Cardiology/ICU)

Hanser, S. B., Larson, S. C., & O'Connell, A. S. (1983). The effect of music on relaxation of expectant mothers during labor. *Journal of Music Therapy, 20*(2), 50-58. (OB/GYN)

Hanser, S. B., & Thompson, L. W. (1994). Effects of music therapy strategy on depressed older adults. *Journal of Gerontology, 49*(6), 265-269. (Alzheimer's)

Haun, M., Mainous, R. O., & Looney, S. W. (2001). Effect of music on anxiety of women awaiting breast biopsy. *Behavioral Medicine, 27*, 127-132. (Surgery)

Haythornwaite, J. A., Lawrence, J. W., & Fauerbach, J. A. (2001). Brief cognitive inerventions for burn pain. *Annals of Behavioral Medicine, 23*(1) 42-29. (Rehabilitation)

Heiser, R. M., Chiles, K., Fudge, M., & Gray, S. E. (1997). The use of music during the immediate postoperative recovery period. *AORN Journal, 65*, 777-785. (Surgery)

Heitz, M. (1992). Effects of music therapy in the postanaesthesia care unit: A nursing intervention. *Journal of Post Anesthesia Nursing, 7*(1), 22-31. (Surgery)

Hilliard, R. E. (2003). The effects of music therapy on the quality and length of life of people diagnosed with terminal cancer. *Journal of Music Therapy, 40*(2), 113-137. (Cancer/Terminal Illness/AIDS)

Holstein, R. E. (2000). The effects of music on patients in a cardiac rehabilitation program. Unpublished master's thesis. San Francisco State University, San Francisco, CA. (Cardiology/ICU)

Howitt, J. W., & Stricker, G. (1966). Objective evaluation of audio-analgesia effects. *Journal of the American Dental Association, 73*, 874-877. (Dental)

Hunt, M. (1997). *How science takes stock: The story of meta-analysis.* New York: Russell Sage Foundation.

Hurt, C. P., Rice, R. R., McIntosh, G. C. & Thaut, M. H. (1998). Rhythmic auditory stimulation in gait training for patients with traumatic brain injury, *Journal of Music Therapy, 35*(4), 228-241. (Rehabilitation)

Jacobson, A. F. (1999). Intradermal normal saline solution, self-selected music, and insertion difficulty effects on intravenous insertion pain. *Heart & Lung, 28*(2), 114-122. (General Hospital)

Joyce, B. A., Keck, J. F., & Gerkensmeyer, J. (2001). Evaluation of pain management interventions for neonatal circumcision pain. *Journal of Pediatric Health Care, 15*(3), 105-111. (Neonatology)

Kaempf, G., & Amodie, M. E. (1989). The effect of music on anxiety. *AORN Journal, 50*(1), 112-118. (Surgery)

Olderog-Millard, K. A., & Smith, J. M. (1989). The influence of group singing therapy on the behavior of Alzheimer's disease patients. *Journal of Music Therapy, 26,* 58-59. (Alzheimer's)

Owens, L. D. (1979). The effects of music on weight loss, crying and physical movement of newborns. *Journal of Music Therapy, 16,* 83-90. (Neonatology)

Palakanis, K.C., DeNobile, J. W., Sweeney, W. B., & Blankenship, C. L. (1994). Effect of music therapy on state anxiety in patients undergoing flexible sigmoidoscopy. *Disease of the Colon & Rectum, 37*(5), 478-481. (General Hospital)

Pelletier, C. L. (2004). The effect of music on decreasing arousal due to stress: A meta-analysis. *Journal of Music Therapy, 41,* 192-214.

Pfaff,V. K, Smith, K. E,. Gowan, D. (1989). The effects of music assisted relaxation on the distress of pediatric cancer patients undergoing bone marrow aspiration. *Children's Health Care, 18,* 232-236. (Cancer/Terminal Illness/AIDS)

Pollack, N. J., & Namazi, K. H. (1992). The effect of music participation on the social Behavior of Alzheimer's disease patients. *Journal of Music Therapy, 29,* 54-67. (Alzheimer's)

Ragneskog, H., Brane, G., Karlsson, I., Kilhgren, M. (1996). Influence of dinner music on food intake and symptoms common in dementia. *Scandinavian Journal of Caring Sciences, 10*(1), 11-17. (Alzheimer's)

Redmond, A. M. (1985). The effect of music on fetal heart rate. *Dissertation Abstracts International B*,46/03, 786. (Fetal)

Reilly, M. P. (1999). Music, a cognitive behavioral intervention for anxiety and acute pain control in the elderly cataract patients. Unpublished doctoral dissertation. University of Texas. San Antonio, TX. (Surgery)

Renzi, C., Peticca, L, & Pescatori, M. (2000). The use of relaxation techniques in the perioperative management of proctological patients: preliminary results. *International Journal of Colorectal disease, 15,* 313-316. (Surgery)

Rider, M. S. (1985). Entrainment mechanisms are involved in pain reduction, muscle relaxation, and music-mediated imagery. *Journal of Music Therapy, 22*(4), 183-192. (Rehabilitation)

Robb, C. (2000). The effect of therapeutic music interventions on the behavior of hospitalized children in isolation: developing a contextual support mode of music therapy. *Journal of Music Therapy, 37*(2), 118-46. (Pediatrics)

Robb, S. L., Nichols, R. J., Rutan, R. L., Bishop, B. L., & Parker, J. C. (1995). The effects of music assisted relaxation on preoperative anxiety. *Journal of Music Therapy, 32*(1), 2-21. (Surgery)

Rosenthal, R. (1984). Meta-analytic procedures for social research. Beverly Hills: Sage Publications.

Rosenthal, R. (1991). Meta-analytic procedures for social research (Rev. edition). Newbury Park, CA: Sage

Rosenthal, R., and Rubin, D. B. (1982). A Simple, General Purpose Display of Magnitude of Experimental Effect. *Journal of Educational Psychology, 74,* 166-169.

Ryan, E. A. (1989). The effect of musical distraction on pain in hospitalized school-aged children. In S. G. Funk, E. M. Tornquist, M. T. Champagne, L. A. Copp, & R. A.

Wiese (Eds.), *Key aspects of comfort. Management of pain, fatigue and nausea* (pp.101-104). New York: Springler. (Pediatrics)

Sabo, C. E., & Michael, S. R. (1996). The influence of personal message with music on anxiety and side effects associated with chemotherapy. *Cancer nursing, 19*(4), 283-289. (Cancer/Terminal Illness/AIDS)

Satt, B. J. (1984). An investigation into the acoustical induction of intrauterine learning. *Dissertations Abstracts International B, 45/05,* 1603. (Fetal)

Schinner, K. M., Chisholm, A. H., Grap, M. J., Siva, P., Hallinan, N., & Lavoie-Hawkins,A. M. (1995). Effects of auditory stimuli on intracranial pressure and cerebral perfusion pressure in traumatic brain injury. *Journal of Neuroscience Nursing, 27*(6), 348-354. (Rehabilitation)

Schneider, N., Schedlowski, M., Schurmeyer, T. H., & Becker, H. (2001). Stress reduction through music in patients undergoing cerebral angiography. *Neuroradiology, 43,* 472-476. (General Hospital)

Schorr, J. A. (1993). Music and pattern change in chronic pain. *Advances in Nursing Science, 15*(4), 27-36. (Rehabilitation)

Schuster, B. L. (1985). The effect of music listening on BP fluctuations in adult hemodialysis patients. *Journal of Music Therapy, 22,* 146-153. (General Hospital)

Schwartz, F., Ritchie, R., Sacks, L. L., & Phillips, C. E. (1998). Music, stress reduction and medical cost savings in the neonatal intensive care unit. In R. R. Pratt & D. E. Grocke (Eds.), *MusicMedicine 3.* Melbourne, Australia: Melbourne University Press. (Neonatology)

Seukeran, D. C., & Vestey, J. P. (1997). The use of music during dermatological surgery. *British Journal of Dermatology, 13*(50), 58-59. (Surgery)

Shapiro, A. G. & Cohen, H. (1986). Auxiliary pain relief during suction curettage. In R. Spintge & R. Droh (Eds.), *Music in Medicine* (pp.227-232). NY: Springer-Verlag. (OB/GYN)

Silber, F. (1999). The influence of background music on the performance of the Mini Mental State Examination with patients diagnosed with Alzheimer's disease. *Journal of Music Therapy, 36*(3),196-206. (Alzheimer's)

Silverman, M. J. (2003). The influence of music on the symptoms of schizophrenia: A meta-analysis. *Journal of Music Therapy, 40,* 27–40.

Smith, G. H.(1986). A comparison of the effects of three treatment interventions on cognitive functioning of Alzheimer's patients. *Music Therapy, 6A,* 41 56. (Alzheimer's)

Smith, M., Casey, L., Johnson, D., Gwede, C., & Riggin, O. Z. (2001). Music as a therapeutic intervention for anxiety in patients receiving radiation therapy.*Oncology Nursing Forum, 28*(5), 855-862. (Cancer/Terminal Illness/AIDS)

Snyder, M. & Olson, J. (1996). Music and hand massage interventions to produce relaxation and reduce aggressive behaviors in cognitively impaired elders: a pilot study. *Clinical Gerontologist, 17*(1), 64-69. (Alzheimer's)

Sohi, B. K. (1997). Differential effectiveness of music-mediated relaxation and guided imagery in post-surgical pain and wound healing. Unpublished Doctoral Dissertation. University of Wisconsin. (Surgery) ontag, L. W., Steele,W. G., & Lewis, M. (1969). The fetal and maternal cardiac response to environmental stress. *Human Development, 12*(1), 1-9. (Fetal)

tandley, J. (1986). Music research in medical/dental treatment: Meta-analysis and clinical implications. *Journal of Music Therapy, 23,* 56–122.

tandley, J. M. (1991). Longterm benefits of music intervention in the NICU: a pilot study. *Journal of the International Association of Music for the Handicapped, 6,* 12-22. (Neonatology)

tandley, J. (1992). Meta-analysis of research in music and medical treatment: Effect size as a basis for comparison across multiple dependent and independent variables. In R. Spintge & R. Droh (Eds.), *MusicMedicine* (pp. 364–378). St. Louis: MMB.

tandley, J. (1996). Music research in medical/dental treatment: An update of a prior meta-analysis. In C. Furman (Ed.), *Effectiveness of music therapy procedures: Documentation of research and clinical practice* (2nd ed., pp. 1–60). Silver Spring, MD: National Association for Music Therapy.

tandley, J. (2000). Music research in medical treatment. In *Effectiveness of music therapy procedures: Documentation of research and clinical practice* (3rd ed., pp. 1–64). Silver Spring, MD: American Music Therapy Association.

tandley, J. M. (2000). The effect of contingent music to increase non-nutritive sucking of premature infants. In J. Loewy (Ed.), *Music therapy in the neonatal intensive care unit.* Cherry Hill, NJ: Jeffrey Books. (Neonatology)

tandley, J. M. (2002). A meta-analysis of the efficacy of music therapy for premature infants. Journal of Pediatric Nursing, 17(2), 107–113.

tandley, J. M. & Moore, R. S. (1995). Therapeutic effects of music and mother's voice on premature infants. *Pediatric Nursing, 21*(6), 509-512. (Neonatology)

tanley, P., & Ramsey, D. (1998). The effects of electronic music-making as a therapeutic activity for improving upper extremity active range of motion. *Occupational Therapy International, 5*(3), 223-237. (Rehabilitation)

teelman, V. M. (1990). Intraoperative music therapy. Effects on anxiety, blood pressure. *AORN-Journal, 52*(5),1026-1034. (Surgery)

tein, A.M. (1991). Music to reduce anxiety during caesarean births. In C. D. Maranto (Ed.), *Applications of Music in Medicine*, (pp.179-190). Washington, D.C.: National Association for Music Therapy, Inc. (OB/GYN)

trauser, J. M. (1997). The effects of music versus silence on measures of state anxiety, perceived relaxation and physiological responses of patients receiving chiropractic interventions. *Journal of Music Therapy*, 34(2), 88-105. (Rehabilitation)

uzuki, A. I. (1998). The effects of music therapy on mood and congruent memory of elderly adults with depressive symptoms. *Music Therapy Perspectives, 16,* 75-80. (Alzheimer's)

zeto, C. K. & Yung, P.M.B. (1999). Introducing and music programme to reduce preoperative anxiety. *British Journal of Theatre Nursing, 9,* 10, 455-459. (Surgery)

ang, C. S., Ko, C. J., Ng, S. M., Chen, S. C. Cheng, K.I., Yu, K.L., & Tseng, C.K. (1993). "Walkman music" during epidural anesthesia. *Gaoxiong Yi Xue Ke Xue Za Zhi, 9* (8), 458-475. (Surgery)

Tanioka, F., Takazawa, T., Kamata, S., Kudo, M., Matasuki, A., & Oyama, T. (1987). Hormonal effect of anxiolytic music in patients during surgical operation under epidural anaesthesia. In R. Spintge & R. Droh (Eds.), Musik in der Medizin (199–204). Heidelberg: Springer-Verlag. (Surgery)

Taylor, L. K., Kuttler, K. L., Parks, T. A., & Milton, D. (1998). The effect of music in the post-anesthesia care unit on pain levels in women who have had abdominal hysterectomies. *Journal of Perianestheria Nursing, 13*, 88-94. (Surgery)

Thaut, M. H. (1985). The use of auditory rhythm and rhythmic speech to aid temporal muscular control in children with gross motor dysfunction. *Journal of Music Therapy, 22*, 129-145. (Rehabilitation)

Thaut, M. H., McIntosh, G. C., Prassas, S. G. & Rice, R. R. (1993). Effect of rhythmic cueing on temporal stride parameters and EMG patterns in hemiparetic gait of stroke patients. *Journal of Neurological Rehabilitation, 7*, 9-16. (Rehabilitation)

Thaut, M. H., McIntosh, G. C., Rice, R. R., Miller, R. A., Rathbun, J., & Brault, J. M. (1995). Rhythmic auditory stimulation in gait training for Parkinson's disease patients. *Movement Disorders, 11*(2), 193-200. (Rehabilitation)

Thaut, M. H., McIntosh, G. C., & Rice, R. R. (1997). Rhythmic facilitation of gait training in hemiparetic stroke rehabilitation. *Journal of Neurological Sciences, 151*, 207-212. (Rehabilitation)

Thaut, M. H., Kenyon, G. P., Hurt, C. P., McIntosh, G. C., & Hoemberg, V. (2002). Kinematic optimization of spatiotemporal patterns in paretic arm training with stroke patients. Neuropsychologia, *40*(7), 1073-1081. (Rehabilitation)

Thomas, D. W., Heitman, R. J., & Alexander, T. (1997). The effects of music on bathing cooperation for residents with dementia. *Journal of Music Therapy, 34*, 248-259. (Alzheimer's)

Tibbs, P. S. (1991). Changes in stress-related behaviors of hospitalized preschoolers during a brachial venipuncture procedure with and without a music therapy program: A replication. Unpublished master's thesis. The University of Mississippi Medical Center, Mississippi. (Pediatrics)

Tusek, D. L., Church, J. M., Strong, S. A., Grass, J. A., & Fazio, V. W. (1997). Guided Imagery: A significant advance in care of patients undergoing elective colorectal surgery. *Diseases of the Colon and Rectum, 40*, 172-178. (Surgery)

Updike, P. (1990). Music therapy results for ICU patients. *Dimensions in Critical Care Nursing, 9*, 39-45. (Cardiology/ICU)

Updike, P.A., & Charles, D. M. (1987). Music Rx: physiological and emotional responses to taped music programs of preoperative patients awaiting plastic surgery. *Annals of Plastic Surgery, 19*(1) p. 29-33. (Surgery)

VanderArk S., Newman, I., & Bell, S. (1983). The effects of music participation on Quality of life of the elderly. *Music Therapy, 3*, 71-81. (Alzheimer's)

Walther-Larsen, S., Diemar, V., & Valentin, N. (1988). Music during regional anesthesia. A reduced need of sedatives. *Regional Anesthesia, 13*(2), 69-71. (Surgery)

Wang, S. M., Kulkarni, L., Dolev, J., & Kain, Z. N. (2002). Music and preoperative anxiety: A randomized controlled study. *Anesthesia and Analgesia, 94*, 1489-1494. (Surgery)

Whipple, J. (2004). Music in intervention for children and adolescents with autism: A meta-analysis. *Journal of Music Therapy, 41*, 90–106.

White, J. M. (1992). Music therapy: An intervention to reduce anxiety in the myocardial infarction patient. *Clinical Nurse Specialist, 6*(2), 58-63. (Cardiology/ICU)

White, J. M. (1999). Effects of relaxing music on cardiac autonomic balance and anxiety after acute myocardial infarction. *American Journal of Critical Care, 8*(4), 220-230. (Cardiology/ICU)

Whittal, J. (1989). The impact of music therapy in palliative care: A quantitative pilot study. In J.A. Martin (Ed.), *The next step forward: Music therapy with the terminally ill* (pp.69-72). Bronx, New York: Calvary Hospital. (Cancer/Terminal Illness/AIDS)

Winter, M. J., Paskin, S., & Baker, T. (1994). Music reduces stress and anxiety of patients in the surgical holding area. *Journal of Post Anesthesia Nursing, 9*, 340-343. (Surgery)

Wolfe, J. R. (1983). The use of music in a group sensory training program for regressed geriatric patients. *Activities, Adaptation, and Aging, 4*(1), 49-61. (Alzheimer's)

Wong, H. L. C., Lopez-Nahas, V., & Molassiotis, A. (2001). Effect of music therapy on anxiety in ventilator-dependent patients. *Heart and Lung, 30*(5), 376-387. (Cardiology/ICU)

Yung, P., Kam, S. C., Lau, B., & Chan, T. (2003). The effects of music in managing preoperative stress for Chinese surgical patients in the operating room holding area: A controlled trial. *International Journal of Stress Management, 10*(1), 64-74. (Surgery)

Zimmer, E. Z., Divon, M.Y., Vilensky, A., Sarna, Z., Peretz, B. A., & Paldi, E. (1982). Maternal exposure to music and fetal activity. European Journal of Obstetrics and Gynecology and Reproductive Biology, *13*(4), 209-213. (Fetal)

Zimmerman, L., Nieveen, J., Barnason, S., & Schmaderer, M. (1996). The effects of music interventions on postoperative pain and sleep in coronary artery bypass graft (CABG) patients. *Scholarly Inquiry in Nursing Practice, 10*(2), 153-174. (Surgery)

Zimmerman, L. M., Pierson, M. A., & Marker, J. (1988). Effects of music on patient anxiety in coronary care units. *Heart and Lung Journal of Critical Care, 17*(5), 560-566. (Cardiology/ICU)

Zimmerman, L., Pozehl, B., Duncan, K., & Schmitz, R. (1989). Effects of music in patients who had chronic cancer pain. *Western Journal of Nursing Research, 11*, 289-309. (Cancer/Terminal Illness/AIDS)